MICROGRAPHIC SYSTEMS

MICROGRAPHIC SYSTEMS

by

Daniel M. Costigan

NMA Reference Series No. 16

National Micrographics Association
8728 Colesville Road, Silver Spring, Maryland 20910
1975

Library of Congress Catalog Card Number: 75-29532.

The National Micrographics Association,
8728 Colesville Road, Silver Spring, Maryland 20910

Printed in the United States of America

*To all whose consciences unite
them in a common cause: more efficient
utilization of the world's resources*

Contents

CHAPTER 10. "SELLING" THE SYSTEM   163

APPENDICES

xi

Illustrations

Chapter 5

Chapter 6

Chapter 7

Daniel M. Costigan

DANIEL M. COSTIGAN is a systems analyst at Bell Laboratories, where he has been involved with micrographic systems and standards development since 1962. The Bell System's pioneering microfilm program for engineering drawings had been implemented just two years earlier, and one of Mr. Costigan's first assignments was to help develop the test apparatus and standards necessary to insure continued improvement in the program's operating efficiency and output quality. More recently, he has become involved in studies aimed at the development of new systems for the more efficient transfer of graphic information in general. His current field of specialization is facsimile communication, in which connection he chairs the joint NMA/Electronic Industries Association Microfilm-Facsimile Standards Committee (TR 29.1). Besides NMA, Mr. Costigan holds membership in the IEEE and in the Telephone Pioneers of America. He is author of a number of published journal and periodical articles, and of the book, *FAX: The Principles and Practice of Facsimile Communication.*

Preface

When I was asked to write this book, my first reaction was to suggest some other people who I thought had better credentials than I to take on a task of this sort. The response I got was—"They're all too busy."

On reflection, I had to accept that explanation to the extent of acknowledging that micrographics is indeed a busy field these days. It has, in fact, been growing steadily busier for a number of years now, and that trend does not appear very likely to change—except possibly to accelerate—in the near future.

In tracing the evolution of what we now refer to as the micrographics industry, several important milestones can be cited. The ones that generally spring to mind are McCarthy's invention of the rotary camera in the 1920s, opening the way to the banking community's use of microfilm as a records retention medium; the subsequent embracing of the medium by libraries for the retention of periodicals; the famed "V-mail" system of World War II; and, most recently, the combining of micrographics with computer technology.

But there is one event that stands out above all of these in explaining the current rapid growth of the industry, and that is the movement that began in earnest sometime around the late 1950s or early '60s to transform microfilm from an essentially "archival" medium to an active systems tool.

I entered the field when that transformation had just got underway, and there could not have been a more exciting time to be initiated into micrographics (or micro*film,* as it was called then). There was a pervasive spirit of innovation that saw, among other things, the emergence of computer output microfilming (COM) as the first totally new departure in microfilming since the rotary camera, and it was during that period—the early to middle 1960s—that microfilm ceased to be merely a branch of industrial photography and emerged as an industry in its own right.

It was my good fortune to have entered the field via the Bell Telephone Laboratories in New York, where I came in contact with Carl E. Nelson and, for a year or so, had the benefit of his able tutelage. Carl, a past president and fellow of NMA, was, until his retirement early in 1963, a Bell Laboratories engineer and the one who had earlier organized the microfilm group in New York as a kind of appendage of the Engineering Standards Department.* He is one of the handful of men who pioneered the use of microfilm as the medium in which engineering drawings are today commonly stored and distributed.

At the beginning of this Preface, I used the word *credentials,* which is generally taken to suggest documentation attesting to particular qualifications. I was using it deferentially, in the more abstract sense of cumulative education, experience, achievements, etc.; and it occurs to me that a point ought to be made here about this matter of credentials (in the broad sense) as it pertains to the person who aspires to a career in micrographic systems planning.

If this book is to be your portal to the world of micrographics, and if you are approaching it with some trepidation because of an unfamiliarity with the technologies of optics, photography, chemistry, automated machines—or whatever other hostile complexities you think may be awaiting you there—don't despair! It has been my observation—and one that I think will be borne out by scanning the author biographies in back issues of *The Journal of Micrographics*—that there is no specific set of prerequisites that can be cited to qualify one for the occupation of micrographic systems planner. (I came to it with a vocational background in electronics and a professional inclination toward a career in journalism).

If you were to ask me what broad qualifications one needs to become an effective practitioner, my answer would be simply—*a willingness to learn, and to accept, unconventional new routines in the physical movement of information, and the confidence to use your imagination to the fullest in applying the available tools.* If you have those qualities, plus some basic guidance (such as you will hopefully get from this book), there is no reason why, with a little effort, you cannot be as competent a systems planner as anyone else.

About the content and slant of this book: I have tried primarily to write it in a way that will make it readable and interesting for the novice, whom I hope it will serve as an effective introduction to micrographic systems planning. But, at the same time, I have tried *not* to "talk down" to those readers who may already have experience in micrographics and who I hope will find the book of equal value as a kind of refresher course. I have sought to avoid, as much as possible, the technical details of how things work, and have placed the emphasis, instead, on how individual system components are selected to meet the needs of the end user, and how they are assembled into a workable whole.

Now, as is customary, let me take just a few short paragraphs to acknowledge the help I had from a number of sources in putting this book together.

Deserving special mention for having tolerated my frequent intrusions

---

*Among other alumni of that original Bell Labs Microfilm group are Hank Frey and Don Avedon, currently the President and Technical Director (respectively) of the NMA.

on their free time with incessant questions are my colleagues at Bell Laboratories—notably Mike Badal, Don Blesse, Bob Burger, Tony Calavas, John Cebak, Allan Gilligan, Bill Lanigan, Ray Misiewicz, Al Pavlick, Charlie Robertshaw, J. C. Noll of the Computing Technology Department, and, of course, Hank Frey, Supervisor of the Micrographic Information Systems Group. A special note of thanks is due also to Bob Williams and Doug Burke for their administrative acquiescence; to June Woods for coordinating the typing of the manuscript; to Gil Davidson of the parent A.T.&T. Company, whose previous writings on the subject of micrographics proved a particularly valuable reference source; and to Bob Horodyski, Charlie Kuhl, Dick Levesque, John O'Sullivan and Chet Allen, all of whom helped me to fill various holes in the raw manuscript.

Especially cooperative among those from whom I sought "outside" help (professional planners, service bureaus, etc.) were "Barney" Barnett, Jim Bateman, Fred Bertsch, Bob Bohner, Joseph E. Britton III, Alex Brunner, Louis DiCrescenzo, Richard Hess, Stan Mackay, Joe Putlock, Fritz Rengel, Marty Screen, Hillard Sutin, John Tupper, and Nick Szabo. In this same category, I also thank all of those other vendors (too numerous to list individually) who generously supplied photographs and descriptions of their commercial products.

Considerable credit for the accuracy and completeness of the final draft is due Don Avedon, NMA's Technical Director, and Mitch Badler, Hub Ballou, Bob Glotfelty, Karl Horwitz, Loretta Kiersky, Mary O'Hara, and Dave Wolf, all of whom expertly critiqued the preliminary draft on behalf of NMA as members of that organization's Publications Committee.

Finally, a collective note of appreciation to the authors of the several articles and books that served me as occasional references and that, in some cases, served also to refresh my memory of certain aspects of micrographics on which I had frankly become rusty.

DMC
(June, 1975)

Introduction

We find ourselves living in a world in which there are grave doubts regarding the continuing availability of natural resources. Moreover, the national economy is under pressure and many businesses are faced with the necessity of increasing their efficiency if they are to survive. It is a time of intense activity for methods and systems analysts in improving the effectiveness of operations, and thus quite naturally a time of heightened interest in micrographic systems.

Micrographics has always held the potential of space savings, simplified distribution, and rapid as well as economical retrieval. Yet, as an industry it has never quite attained the recognition and utilization that had been forecast for it. For the most part, the manufacturers of micrographic equipment and supplies have been reasonably responsive to users' needs. Computer output microfilm and transparent photoconductive (TPC) technology are examples of developments that have expanded our horizons. It remains, however, for the user to take greater advantage of such advancements in micrographics technology and to employ them creatively in improving information systems.

This can only be accomplished if we increase the availability of information on micrographic systems; and that is the principle objective of this book. For the novice, it serves as a road map, honestly and objectively pointing out pitfalls as well as advantages. For the experienced micrographics practitioner or systems analyst, it serves as a reaffirmation of the faith, lending substance to many of the analysis techniques that are often taken for granted. As both an officer of the NMA and a long-standing colleague of the author, I view the book with considerable pride. It contributes to the body of knowledge on micrographics at a time when that knowledge is being increasingly sought. It will have a positive impact on both the growth of the micrographics industry and the strengthening of the business community. Finally, it represents a milestone for the educational efforts of the National Micrographics Association.

Henry C. Frey
President,
National Micrographics Association

Chapter 1
What Is A Micrographic System?

Elements of a Basic System • The Microform •
Filming Facilities • Processing Facilities • Duplicating • Display and Reproduction Equipment

Some cynics may say of the adjective *micrographic* that it is nothing more than a sophisticated substitute for *microfilm.* However, there is more to it than that. The trouble with the suffix *film* is that it is somewhat confining. In some so-called micro*film* systems, the microimages are contained on paper or other nonfilm media. Moreover, where the image storage medium is, in fact, film, that fact may be a relatively minor point in consideration of the system as a whole.

Graphic, or *Graphics,* is a bit more descriptive inasmuch as it gives us the broader picture of the recording and reproduction of images in various ways, using various media.

A *micrographic system,* then, can be defined as *an information system that utilizes the special advantages of microimaging in the areas of space saving, reproducibility, durability, file integrity and automated retrieval.*

It follows that the plural *micrographics* is preferred to *microfilm* as a noun when the reference is more general.

I. Elements of a Basic System

An example of a basic micrographic system is the routine microfilming of documents that are no longer needed for regular reference, and can therefore be destroyed, but a record of which must be retained for legal or other purposes. This would be truly a micro*film* system in the traditional sense because its primary purpose is merely to preserve documents as microimages on film. Its principal advantage is that it requires only a tiny

1

fraction of the storage space that would be needed for retention of the original paper documents.

The elements of such a system—applicable to micrographic systems in general—are:

(1) *the program:* How are the affected documents located for "weeding"? At what intervals does microfilming take place? etc.

(2) *the microform:* Which of the available physical forms of microimage media will be used? In this example, probably roll film, and possibly just the roll that had been in the camera (no duplicates).

(3) *filming facilities:* This may be a camera and trained operator on-premises or an arrangement with an outside service firm.

(4) *processing facilities:* May exist on-premises, or the work may be done outside whether the camera is on-premises or not.

(5) *duplicating and distribution:* Are duplicate microforms needed for added safekeeping or for occasional reference at branch offices? Again, this may be handled on-premises with suitable equipment, or by an outside service firm.

(6) *filing and retrieval facilities:* In this example, probably just a cabinet (or cabinets) of drawers, located in some remote corner of the office or building.

(7) *display and reproduction equipment:* If there is even the remotest possibility of future reference to any of the microfilmed documents, at least one suitable reader (viewer) would have to be conveniently available. Where duplicate files are maintained at branch locations, each would probably have a reader. Where reference is more frequent and eye-readable prints ("blowbacks") may be required, hard copy print capability may be necessary at each location where a file is maintained.

A typical configuration of such a system is depicted graphically in Figure 1.1.

The system just described would be termed an *archival* system, because its principal purpose is simply to *store* information to which access is comparatively infrequent ("inactive" information). It should be emphasized at this point that such a system is by no means typical of the major use being made of micrographics today. It merely serves to provide a rudimentary look at the subject before proceeding to a more detailed analysis.

In a more active system, a different microform might have been selected—perhaps a multi-image form like *microfiche,* or a single-image form like an E.A.M. aperture card with one document page per card. The various microforms will be discussed in greater detail in the section that follows.

In a somewhat different systems approach, the actual input may be computer-generated data fed by the computer directly to a COM (Computer Output Microfilming) device, which amounts to an automated camera that never sees an original paper document. COM is, in fact, a particularly important aspect of micrographics that will be covered in detail in subsequent chapters.

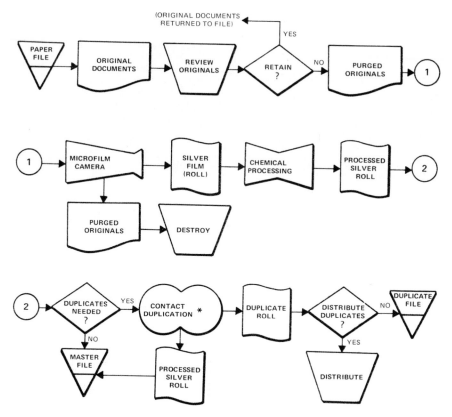

*Indicate number of duplicates made if more than one.

Fig. 1-1. Flowchart of a basic micrographic system, the objective of which is to retain, for legal purposes, microimages of documents that have been slated for destruction as a space-saving move. System flowcharting will be covered in greater detail in Chapter 9.

The remainder of this chapter will concentrate on five of the seven basic system elements identified above, the objective being to illustrate the variety that is possible in the make-up of a micrographic system. The five are *the microform, filming facilities, processing facilities, duplicating,* and *display and reproduction equipment.* Discussion of the continuing program (filming and updating schedules, etc.), distribution, and filing and retrieval will be reserved for subsequent chapters.

As there are various other publications available from the National Micrographics Association that cover each subject in somewhat greater depth, the discussions that follow will be generally in the nature of an overview. This is, in fact, a rule that will be followed throughout the remainder of this book—wherever it is felt that it would be redundant to dwell on subject matter that is adequately covered elsewhere. A list of suggested additional readings—NMA and other—will be given at the end of each chapter.

II. The Microform

The various microimage media, often grouped together under the general heading of *"microfilm"*, exist in several formats. Thus, the term *microform* is preferred as the general handle. It is important to understand that the term implies *end use.* For example, roll film can be—and often is—a microform in its own right. But if it is to be converted to some other form before its actual use, it is this final form to which the term *microform* applies.

Following are brief descriptions of each of the currently standard microforms.

1. *Roll Film*

Except for the reel itself, which is simply a molded plastic holder for a roll of film, and except for the fact that it contains processed microimages ready for viewing and reproduction, *roll film* is identical in form to that in which the raw film stock is usually purchased for use in micrographic cameras.* The standard widths in which the raw stock is available are 8, 16, 35, 70 and 105 millimeters, all of which have found application in micrographic systems, but two of which—16 and 35 mm—tend to predominate in roll systems. The traditional standard length of the film on a reel is 100 feet. However, longer lengths are fast becoming more common, particularly as new, thinner films come into wider use. Typical reels are shown in Figure 1.2.

Fig. 1-2. Typical roll microforms: 16 and 35 millimeter.

There are three more or less fundamental characteristics that distinguish black-and-white roll "microfilm" from that which would ordinarily be used in, for example, a motion picture camera: (1) it has a comparatively fine-grain emulsion to maximize image resolution, (2) it has a comparatively

---

*Raw (unexposed) film generally comes on a metal *spool,* designed to provide a degree of protection against spurious light.

high contrast (narrow tonal range) characteristic, and (3) it is likely to be (but is not necessarily) nonperforated—i.e., it has no sprocket holes.

The images can be arranged on roll film in a variety of ways, but certain arrangements have become standard. On 35 mm film, for example, the individual frames are normally arranged single file along the length of the film, the short dimension of the frame occupying the width of the film, with a small margin at each side. The standard 35 mm frame measures approximately 1.20 x 1.62 inches (approximately 30.5 x 41.2 mm) and its center is about two inches from the center of the adjacent frame. The spacing between microfilmed newspaper pages is about half that length, and, in some applications, letter size documents are recorded in a grid format, usually 4 to 8 pages to a frame. These latter formats are known as "4-up" and "8-up" respectively.

On 16 mm film, there is more variety of image placement. Images may be in-line or side-by-side on the film, and either the long or short dimension of the document image may lie parallel with the film length. The four most common arrangements are shown in Figure 1.3.

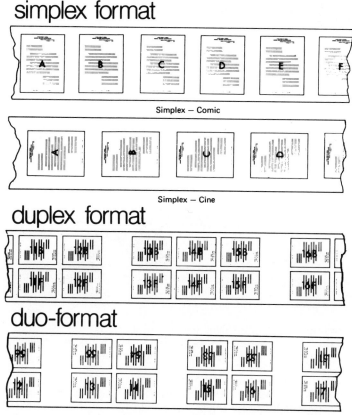

simplex format

Simplex — Comic

Simplex — Cine

duplex format

duo-format

Fig. 1-3. Four common image arrangements on 16mm roll film. The terms "comic" and "cine" derive from frame sequences characteristic of comic strips and motion picture films respectively.

5

2. Cartridges and Cassettes

Cartridges and Cassettes are rigid enclosures containing rolls of film (usually 16 mm), the distinction being that a cartridge is "single-ended" and contains only one core, the film being drawn from it and temporarily stored in a take-up chamber on the reader, and then rewound after use, whereas a cassette contains separate sections and separate *cores* (plastic hubs on which the film is wound) for feed and take-up, and therefore, need not be rewound after use. The two are illustrated in Figure 1.4.

Fig. 1-4. Cartridges (top) and cassettes (bottom) are microforms consisting of roll film in rigid enclosures.

The traditional standard film length for both is 100 feet, but greater lengths are available when film less than 5 mil. in thickness is used. The same image arrangements apply as for film on reels.

A word on nomenclature: although purists will contend that the terms *reel, cartridge,* and *cassette* pertain only to the rigid enclosures that house the film, it has come to be generally accepted that these terms apply as well to specific *roll type microforms.* It is, in fact, this latter usage that will prevail throughout the remainder of this book. The term *roll* will be used generically to apply to reels, cartridges and cassettes alike.

3. Microfiche

Microfiche, often referred to simply as "fiche" (pronounced "feesh"), is a sheet of film containing multiple images in a grid pattern. It exists in various sizes and grid formats, the most common of which currently is the International "A6," 105 x 148 mm size (approximately 4 x 6 inches), with a grid formatted to accommodate 98 images per fiche, each image a 24X linear reduction of a letter-size page. This is also the NMA, ISO and ANSI Standard. (See Figure 1.5.) Higher reduction grids—270 48x-reduced images, for example—appear to be growing in popularity, particularly in applications where the film images are computer-generated. Fiche* containing very large numbers of greatly reduced images are commonly referred to as *ultrafiche.*

Regardless of size or format, all fiche intended for manual retrieval contain an eye-readable "header" that identifies the content. The header can be color-coded to aid retrieval.

The master fiche are usually produced in one of two ways: (1) the images are recorded on 105 mm reel film, which is cut into 148 mm lengths during or after processing, or (2) the images are recorded on 16 mm reel film, which is "stripped-up" into fiche format after processing.

Fiche offers one very interesting capability that should not be overlooked in planning a system: all of the multiple images contained on a single fiche—which can run from several hundred to a few thousand in the case of an ultrafiche format—can be simultaneously duplicated in a matter of seconds in one simple operation.

Fig. 1-5. Microfiche—or "fiche"—is a sheet of film containing multiple images in a grid array. An eye-readable "header" identifies the content.

4. Jackets

Fiche's closest kin in terms of format is "jacketed" microfilm, the jacket being a transparent plastic carrier for strips of film cut from reels. The strips are held in place by a sleeve arrangement. The principal advantages a

---

*The words *fiche* and *microfiche* may be either singular or plural.

7

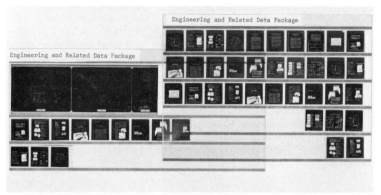

Fig. 1-6. Jackets resemble fiche, but are actually thin, transparent holders, compartmented to accommodate strips of film cut from rolls.

jacket has over fiche are that it can be edited and can contain mixed widths of film. Figure 1.6 shows two jacket arrangements.

5. *Aperture Cards*

An aperture card is a paper card into which has been cut a rectangular aperture (or apertures) within which frames of film can be mounted. The standard size is that of an EAM* tab card, and the typical aperture is one arranged to accommodate a 35 mm frame. The film frame is held in place either by pressure-sensitive adhesive or by insertion into a transparent sleeve. (See Figure 1.7.)

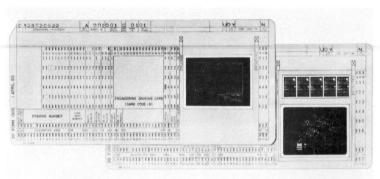

Fig. 1-7. Aperture cards containing "chips" of film. Within limits, they can be machine-sorted like standard tab cards.

Copy cards are aperture cards already containing unexposed chips of special copy film for contact duplication purposes. Since both aperture and copy cards are, in effect, "raw materials" that are purchased in bulk for use in a micrographic system, a third term—*image card*—should technically apply to either of these basic cards once it contains a developed image. Chapter 5 contains a discussion of the use of aperture and copy cards in a system.

---

*Electric Accounting Machine.

8

6. *Micro-opaques*

In format, micro-opaques are like fiche, but are opaque paper stock rather than transparent film. They offer the advantage of being able to contain a separate set of images on each side, but have the disadvantages of being virtually impossible to duplicate and of requiring comparatively high intensity illumination for viewing and printing. (See Figure 1.8.)

* * *

There are, in addition to these standard microforms, some nonstandard ones such as *chips* and *scrolls.* "Chips" are, as the name implies, simply pieces of film that may contain optical or magnetic coding in addition to images. "Scrolls" are simply rolls of extra wide film (usually 105 mm) found in some automated retrieval systems and usually integral to the system's search mechanism. Both of these forms are in very limited use at the present time.

Each of the standard microforms tends to fall into certain broad application categories. 16 mm roll film, for example, is generally used for checks, correspondence, accounting data, and the like, whereas 35 mm roll film is the normal standard for preserving newspapers and journals on film in libraries. Fiche is well-suited for periodicals, reports and catalogs; jackets tend to thrive in "profile" applications such as personnel files; and aperture cards commonly contain engineering drawings.

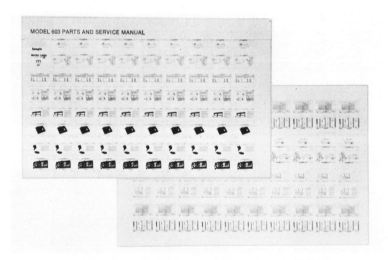

Fig. 1-8. The micro-opaque resembles microfiche, but is not transparent. A separate set of images can be printed on each side. Viewing and reproduction requires reflection of light from the image surface.

9

III. Filming Facilities

There are a variety of cameras designed specifically for microfilming, but all fall into one of two basic classifications: *planetary* and *rotary.* With a planetary camera, the material to be filmed is laid out on a flat *plane,* * whereas, with a rotary—or *flow*—camera, the material is filmed while in motion. The latter uses a precision mechanical feed arrangement to continuously photograph the document through a narrow slit while both document and film are in synchronous motion.

The planetary camera is usually arranged with the camera *head*—containing the lens, shutter, film chamber and advance mechanism—looking down upon a horizontal *copyboard,* on which are laid the documents to be filmed. It includes strategically placed floodlights for subject illumination, and may have provision for vertical adjustment of the camera head to enable filming at various reductions.

Because of the possible effects of vibration and the use of mechanical synchronization in rotary cameras, image resolution is generally inferior to that of planetary cameras, though usually adequate for the types of material for which rotaries are intended (checks, business correspondence, etc.). The output of rotary cameras is always roll film.

Planetary cameras vary widely in design and complexity. For example, some are capable of automatically positioning the sequential exposures in grid format on the film for fiche production *(step-and-repeat* cameras), and others have a built-in film processing capability. The latter are referred to as *camera-processors.* The output of the basic planetary camera is roll film. Camera-processors may output finished unit microforms such as aperture cards or fiche.

By far the most sophisticated filming device used in micrographic systems today is the Computer Output Microfilmer (COM), which includes a microfilm camera as just one component of its total make-up. In essence a computer peripheral, the COM device functions as a planetary camera, but one in which an electronic display device (a CRT, for example) has been substituted for the copyboard. Digital data from magnetic tape—or direct from the computer—is converted to light images on the face of the display device, and it is these fleeting images that are recorded on the film. Discussion of how COM fits into a micrographic system will be reserved for later chapters.

Typical examples of the various types of cameras are shown in Figure 1.9.

IV. Processing Facilities

Except in the case of a camera-processor, the next separate step in the production of the microform is the processing of the film. Since we are dealing with silver halide film, as in ordinary photography, standard processing techniques and chemistry apply. Obviously, the specific "bath"

---

*Whether this is how the planetary camera gets its name is open to speculation. An alternative explanation is that the name pertains to the manner in which the lights and camera head are arranged like planets around the fixed, flat copyboard.

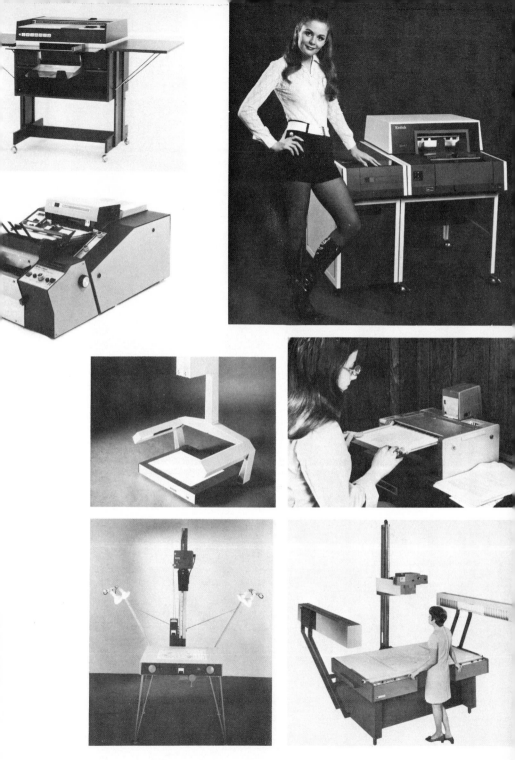

Fig. 1-9, (a). Various types of cameras used for microfilming. 1-4, rotary cameras; 5-7, planetary cameras.

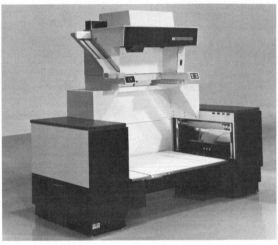

Fig. 1-9, (b). Types of cameras used for microfilming. 1-3, step and repeat cameras; 4-6, special cameras.

1	2
3	4
5	6

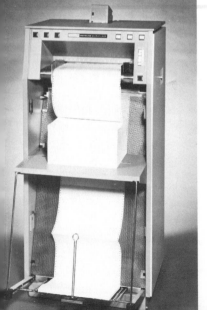
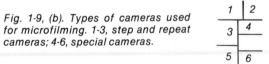

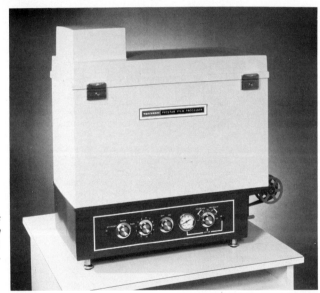

Fig. 1-10 (a). Examples of the types of film processors used in micrographic systems.

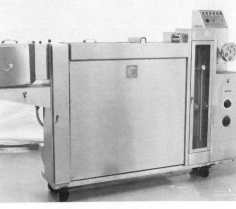

Fig. 1-10, (b). Other micrographic film processors.

recipes and timings will depend on film emulsion specifications. Other parameters, such as thoroughness of washing and stability of water temperatures, will be dictated by the system's end quality requirements.

Processing is the production step most likely to be handled by an outside service bureau, particularly in smaller systems. However, completely automatic processors, some compact enough for use in an office environment, are available from a number of vendors. A selection is shown in Figure 1.10.

It is important to recognize that in-house film processing entails more than just the purchase of a machine to do the job. Special plumbing may be required, which, in turn, will usually involve compliance with local waste disposal ordinances. There is also the continuing need to replenish and refresh processing chemicals and to keep a close watch on the quality of the processed images. These and other specific processing considerations will be discussed in Chapters 8 and 9.

V. Duplicating

Duplicate microforms are required for various reasons. The working file of a micrographic system may consist entirely of duplicates, particularly where it is one of several branch files having the same content. Even in systems having only a single working file, it may consist of duplicates because of a requirement that the master microforms be committed to a security vault.

In many systems, expendable duplicates are produced on demand at the file for point-of-use reference—at an employee's desk, for example.

Duplication of microforms normally involves use of special films intended strictly for copying purposes, and is usually a *contact* process—i.e., exposure takes place with the master microform in direct physical contact with the copy film. One popular type of copy film is *diazo,* which is developed by ammonia gas. Another is *vesicular* film, which is developed by heat. Silver halide film is also used for contact duplication, but primarily in *micropublishing,* where comparatively large volumes of high quality duplicates are required. Silver duplicates naturally require the same chemical processing as the camera masters, which is the main reason that more convenient nonsilver copy films are favored in relatively low volume duplication situations. In aperture card systems, where each frame of film is separately card-mounted, silver duplicates can be conveniently produced at the camera in the filming phase simply by taking multiple sequential exposures of each document page. When later mounted in aperture cards, they serve as duplicate master image cards for distribution.

There are duplicators for every type of microform. They vary in duplicating volume and in degree of automation depending on whether they are designed for *production* or *demand* duplicating configurations. The latter are relatively compact and are designed for use in an office environment. Examples are shown in Figure 1.11.

15

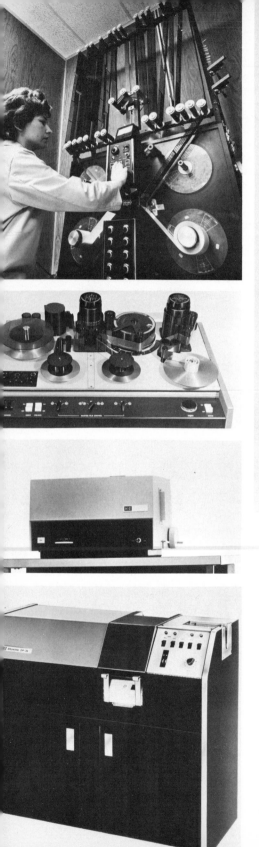

Fig. 1-11, (a). Examples of duplicators used for contact duplication of master microforms. 1-3, roll-to-roll duplicators; 4-5, aperture card duplicators.

1	
2	3
4	
5	

$$\begin{array}{c|c} & 2 \\ & \overline{3} \\ 1 & 4 \end{array}$$

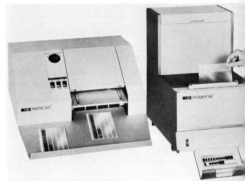

Fig. 1-11 (b). Microfiche duplicators.

VI. Display and Reproduction Equipment

Possibly because libraries were among the earlier users of microfilm as an active information medium, the devices for viewing microimages are referred to as *readers*. The typical reader is a desk-top display unit designed to accept a specific microform. It contains a light source and optical system by which it rear-projects the microimage on a built-in translucent viewing screen. There are also "multimedia" readers, designed to accept two or more different microforms, and there are readers that *front*-project onto reflective opaque screens. (See Figure 1.12.)

Readers are available in a variety of magnifications, the determining factors being the reduction at which the microimages were recorded and the size of the viewing screen. Many readers have provision for interchanging lenses to satisfy varying user requirements.

Reader-printers are, as the name implies, readers having a printing capability. In situations where the user wants to "capture" the screen image in the form of a paper print, the reader-printer accomplishes this in response to the press of a button. The sensitized print paper is fed from a roll (or possibly from a "magazine" of pre-cut sheets) within the device. The portion exposed to the projected image is automatically advanced through a developer and delivered to the user from a slot at the front or side of the unit. The whole process normally takes a matter of seconds. Figure 1.13 shows a typical selection of commercial reader-printers.

There are also *enlarger-printers* (Figure 1.14), which are intended strictly for printing and do not have a reading capability, *per se,* although a viewing screen may be provided for focusing and aligning the image to be printed. Enlarger-printers are most likely to be found in relatively high volume reproduction environments.

* * *

These, then, are the basic elements of a micrographic system. Obviously, even the most basic system would be incomplete without the physical means for filing and retrieving the microforms, and without an underlying set of procedures on which to base the use and maintenance of the system. These aspects and others will be covered in subsequent chapters.

The next chapter is really a continuation of this one, except that it approaches the question, "What is a micrographic system?" a little differently. It examines basic objectives and illustrates ways in which micrographics may be expected to improve present operating methods in a variety of real situations.

Fig. 1-12, (a). Some of the readers available for viewing roll microfilm.

Fig. 1-12, (b). A selection of microfiche readers.

Fig. 1-13. Reader-printers give the user the option of merely viewing the enlarged micro-image on a screen, or obtaining a paper print of it.

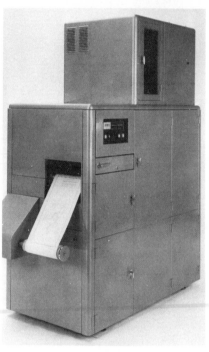

Fig. 1-14. Enlarger-printers differ from reader-printers in that they do not ordinarily have viewing screens. They are used primarily in central file and high-volume production situations.

Suggested Additional Reading

Boyd, Sherman H., "Film Requirements for Computer Output Microfilm." *NMA Proceedings, 1972.* Silver Spring, Md.: NMA. pp.III-35—III-49.
Cassidy, W.J., "Microfilm Cameras: Turning Mountains Into Molehills." *Office Product News,* January 17, 1975. p.11.
Conners, R.J., "Microfilm Reader/Printers: Versatile Office Tools." *Office Product News,* September 20, 1974. p.25.
Connolly, F., "Microfilm Jacket Systems for Up to Date Information." *Office Product News,* June 21, 1974. p.15.
Harmon, George H., "Notes About Microfilm." (series of articles in *Reproduction Review and Methods,* commencing May, 1974).
Information Through Microcopy. Holyoke, Mass.: Scott Graphics, 1972. 18p.
Introduction to Micrographics. Silver Spring, Md.: NMA, 1973. 28p.
Proctor, James A., "Fundamental Micrographics—An Overview." *NMA Proceedings, 1973.* Silver Spring, Md.: NMA. pp. II-3—II-9.
Rice, E. Stevens, *Fiche and Reel.* Ann Arbor, Mich.: Xerox University Microfilms, 1972. 22p.
Roeglin, G., "Microfilm Readers: Moving Toward the Future." *Office Product News,* April 19, 1974. p.51.
Spigai, F.G., *The Invisible Medium: The State of the Art of Microform and a Guide to the Literature.* Stanford, Cal. and Washington, D.C.: ERIC Clearinghouse on Media and Technology, and ERIC Clearinghouse on Library and Information Sciences, March 1973. 40p.
Williams, Bernard J.S. *Miniaturized Communications: A Review of Microforms.* London, England: Library Association, 1970. 190p.

Chapter 2
System Objectives

Some   Representative   Systems   •   *Advanced Systems*

In the preceding chapter, a basic micrographic system was defined by illustration, and the example given was the use of microfilm as a space-saving surrogate in the retention of inactive documents. Its ability to con-serve valuable space is, of course, just one of many reasons for considering micrographics as an alternative to paper in the records management and information processing environments. This chapter will examine the principal advantages—namely (1) improved file integrity, (2) in-creased speed of service, (3) improved space utilization, for *active* as well as inactive materials, (4) reduced mailing bulk, (5) insurance against dis-aster, and (6) reduced labor.

With the possible exception of number 5, each of these advantages translates into cost savings, with the net saving over previous methods de-pending on the particular circumstances in each case. Where file activity is extremely heavy, for example, the improved file integrity offered by the micrographics approach will reduce costs attributable to loss or misfiling of originals, and the resulting savings can justify any added costs the new system may incur over the old. File integrity, in this instance, means keeping the file intact and in good order, and this is accomplished in the micrographics approach by the fact that masters never have to be removed from the file for temporary lending or for reproduction at another location. They can be reproduced, on demand *at the file,* as screen images, dupli-cate microfilm, or enlarged prints. It is easy to see how this will, in turn, in-crease the speed of service by minimizing the waiting time that might otherwise have resulted from a document's being temporarily out-of-file or its having been transferred to less accessible storage.

The same characteristic that causes people to look to micrographics where storage space has become a problem—namely, the reduction in bulk it offers—also makes it a natural in situations where large volumes of paper documentation must be distributed without delay to distant locations. As any manager of a high volume, tight deadline publishing operation will attest, this can be a costly proposition. Thus, where microimages are acceptable as a reproduction medium or for end use, micrographics can be a viable solution to this problem.

A micrographics system intended as insurance against disaster would be close kin to the basic system described in Chapter 1. In most instances, it would be a micro*film* system, pure and simple, and would amount to the production—one-time or ongoing—of a microimage duplicate of a valuable paper* file for safekeeping at a separate location. It would qualify as a *system* to the extent that it required a continuing program of new filming and perhaps periodic review and purging. In an active micrographic system, this protection is generally provided automatically through the dispersal of duplicate working files.

Micrographics saves labor in several ways, but two factors predominate:
(1) the reduction in sheer bulk afforded by miniaturization of records, and thus a reduction in search and handling effort;
(2) the relative ease with which micrographic systems lend themselves to automation.

I.   *Some Representative Systems*

In the preceding chapter, we looked at what constitutes a basic micrographic system and defined the principal broad objectives of micrographic systems in general. Now let's briefly examine six actual systems, one for each of the broad objectives just discussed, identifying the specific objectives of each. Bear in mind that, although a particular objective is stressed in each case, invariably the system will yield other benefits of equal weight or of a secondary nature.

1.   *Improved file integrity*

A major university library finds that it can insure the integrity of its microfilm collection while effectively meeting students' research needs by taking advantage of the availability of relatively low cost microimage duplicating equipment. Most of the masters are on standard microfiche (up to 98 images on a 4x6 inch transparency), which means that a typical request will usually not exceed four to five duplicate fiche (one full, average-length book). Thus, by providing the student with a handfull of expendable duplicates, reproduced on demand from the master, the latter remains on file and is readily available to service subsequent requests for the same material.

Masters are obtained from micropublishers, and readers and reader-printers are provided within the library for student use. A flow chart of the basic system is shown in Figure 2.1.

---

*Throughout this book, the word *paper* will be used somewhat loosely to describe original documents that are subject to microfilming. Obviously, the physical base material of original documents need not be paper exclusively. Engineering drawings, for example, are generally produced on a cloth or plastic base.

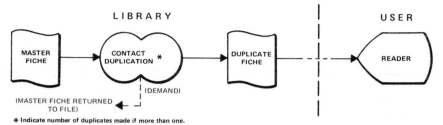

Fig. 2.1. Flowchart of a micrographic system for safeguarding a library's microform collection by making it available as duplicates, produced on demand.

2. Increased speed of service

A large department store in Atlanta, Georgia, has adopted micrographics as a means of ensuring fast turnaround time on customers' queries regarding recent purchases. For example, a customer who has just received a charge statement may phone to question the accuracy of one of the charges. Or there may be some question on what purchased item a particular charge pertains to. If the store still retained its records only in paper form, the service clerk would have to leave the phone and initiate a physical file search for the applicable records while the customer waited patiently for a reply. With microfilm, the average turnaround time for answering an inquiry is about one minute.

The process starts with daily microfilming of sales tickets, batched according to cash register number. Filming is done on a 16 mm rotary camera, and, after processing, the film is put in cartridges and delivered to the store's Customer Service Department. When a customer makes an inquiry, he or she is asked for the reference number that appears beside the transaction on the charge statement, the first three digits of which happen to be the number of the cash register at which the transaction was made. Given that number, the service clerk locates the appropriate cartridge, inserts it in a motorized reader, and, within a matter of seconds, has the related sales ticket on the screen before her. Most questions can be resolved to the customer's satisfaction from the information on the sales ticket alone.

A flowchart of the basic system is shown in Figure 2.2.

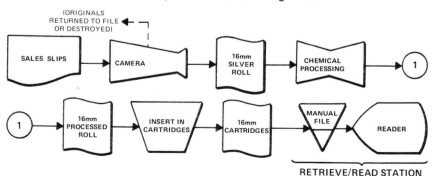

Fig. 2.2 Flowchart of a micrographic system used by a department store to facilitate fast turnaround on inquiries from customers. Microfilmed sales slips form the basic record for referencing.

3. *Improved space utilization*

A 900-bed hospital complex realized an initial gain of some 2500 square feet of valuable floor space when it decided to microfilm a backlog of paper documents that were already beginning to overflow from storage rooms into hallways. The alternative would have been to rent outside storage space. As of 1974, nearly 20 million documents had been microfilmed, about a quarter of them in an initial crash program, and the remainder under a continuing in-house program that was implemented later.

The in-house program covers documents of several different departments—accounting, radiography, electrocardiography, etc. Most of the records dealing with individual patients consist of strips of 16 mm film in transparent jackets that are easily duplicated (1:1) to meet requests for copies of a patient's records. Readers are located throughout the hospital complex for convenience in viewing the microfilmed records.

The continuing program as presently configured is depicted schematically in Figure 2.3.

Fig. 2.3. Flowchart of a micrographic system adopted to regain valuable space in a hospital complex by reducing bulky paper records to microform. Separate records are in the form of jacketed strips of 16mm film.

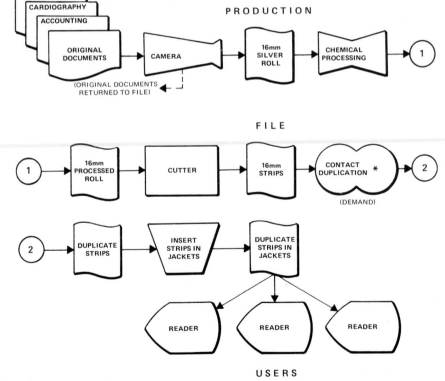

* Indicate number of duplicates made if more than one.

4. Reduced mailing bulk

To keep its several thousand registered dealers informed on the availability of replacement parts, a large manufacturer of small gasoline engines distributes, in an average month, enough new and revised pages to update nearly 30,000 copies of its official parts catalog. Each mailing contains up to 16 pages and, on a paper basis, would cost 22 cents in postage and slightly more than that for preparation and printing. The total annual cost was running in excess of $200,000 until a microfilm program replaced the paper distribution system in 1973.

Today, a set of microfiche containing *twice* the amount of information formerly contained in the paper shipments costs less than half as much to mail. Moreover, this considerably smaller package goes first class (as opposed to third class bulk rate for the former paper parcels), with the result that distribution time is reduced appreciably. The production and distribution aspects of this system are depicted schematically in Figure 2.4.

Fig. 2.4. Production and distribution aspects of a microfiche parts catalog system, adopted by the vendor to save costs in distributing catalog updates to widely scattered dealerships.

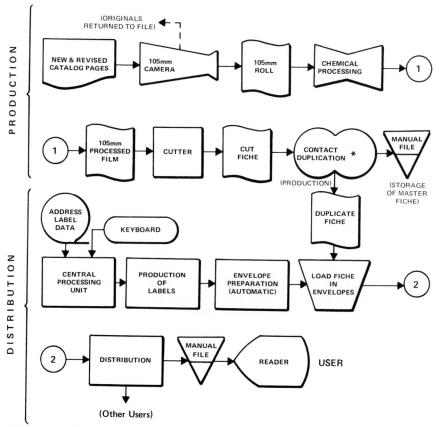

* Indicate number of duplicates made if more than one.

5. Insurance against disaster

An irreplaceable collection of rare books, manuscripts, etc., at one of the country's larger public libraries has been steadily deteriorating as a result of physical handling and natural chemical processes. It is just a matter of time before parts of the collection are beyond saving.

Fortunately, the collection has had some forward-looking guardians who, as far back as the 1930s, began a microfilming program in which special mechanical aids were devised to permit filming the pages of bound books without straining the fragile bindings. To date, some 75,000 rolls of 35 mm film have been completed, and, as long as there are funds to support it, the work will continue at the current rate of 1 million frames a year. As a result, long after the original works have become too fragile to handle, their contents will still be accessible via microfilm.

6. Reduced labor

The correspondence files of a business firm in England consisted of some two million documents when it was decided to microfilm them and destroy the originals. Because of its unwieldy size, maintenance of the original paper file required a full time staff of 11 people. Since the conversion to microfilm, the number has been reduced to three.

II. Advanced Systems

For the most part, the systems outlined so far have entailed the methodical conversion of paper documents to microimages for subsequent manual retrieval from a miniaturized file, the microimages being referenced with the aid of relatively simple microform readers. Various technological advances in recent years have made possible the development and implementation of more complex systems, the advantages of which usually outweigh the added complexity. Two examples of such systems are described briefly in the paragraphs that follow.

1. Semiautomated retrieval of specific documents by an integral logic mechanism.

An electric utility in an eastern U.S. city found that it could substantially speed up its emergency operations by converting its electrical distribution maps to microimages in aperture cards and providing the means to retrieve specific cards automatically by keyboard selection. It works this way: a field crew has been dispatched to the scene of an electrical emergency—perhaps a break in a main conduit that runs under the street. Upon arrival, the crew finds that it needs additional information before it can commence work on the problem. The crew chief radios a dispatcher who has control of the microfilmed maps. Knowing the field crew's location, the dispatcher can retrieve the applicable distribution map in a matter of seconds simply by keying the appropriate code on a manual keyboard. The retrieval device, under the control of its own self-contained logic, responds by "liberating" the desired image card (or cards) from among the thousands contained in the mechanized file. The retrieved card is thereupon inserted in a reader, and the dispatcher is able immediately to communicate the required information to the crew in the field.

From the end of keying to the appearance of the selected image on the screen, the average elapsed time is only about 3 seconds. Total turnaround time from reception of the field crew's request to the dispatcher's response with the needed information can be less than a minute. When reference to the retrieved map is completed, the card is manually returned to the mechanized file, where it can be reinserted in any randomly selected location.

A flow chart of the system is shown in Figure 2.5.

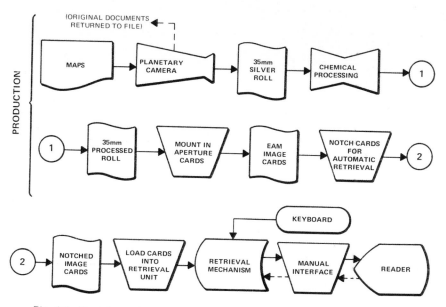

Fig. 2.5. Flowchart of a micrographic system utilizing semiautomated retrieval of microforms to expedite access to map data in an emergency repair situation.

2. Computer-aided, fully automated data retrieval by subject

In its daily operations, the Outside Plant Engineering Department of a large telephone company has to make frequent reference to an extensive and highly fluid data base of policies, practices and procedures. To improve retrieval efficiency, one company recently adopted a totally automated micrographic system in which a dedicated minicomputer is utilized in an index searching capacity to ensure retrieval of all up-to-date pertinent data, as required.

At the heart of the system is the microform data base, consisting of specially notch-coded microfiche sheets contained *within* an automated retrieval-display unit. With provision for sufficient core memory, as many as 128 of these units, each complete with selector keyboard, computer interface, print capability, and a duplicate of the data base, can be connected to the central minicomputer—either locally or remotely via standard data communication links. Each unit has capacity for storing 167,000 document

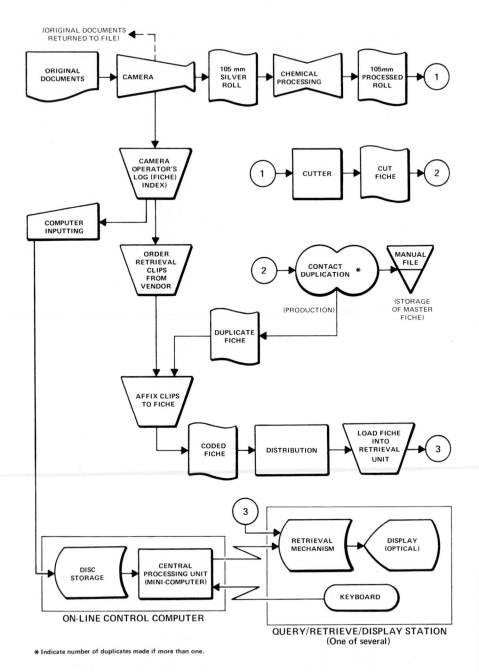

(ORIGINAL DOCUMENTS RETURNED TO FILE)

ORIGINAL DOCUMENTS → CAMERA → 105 mm SILVER ROLL → CHEMICAL PROCESSING → 105mm PROCESSED ROLL → 1

CAMERA OPERATOR'S LOG (FICHE INDEX)

1 → CUTTER → CUT FICHE → 2

COMPUTER INPUTTING

ORDER RETRIEVAL CLIPS FROM VENDOR

2 → CONTACT DUPLICATION ＊ → MANUAL FILE

(PRODUCTION)

(STORAGE OF MASTER FICHE)

DUPLICATE FICHE

AFFIX CLIPS TO FICHE → CODED FICHE → DISTRIBUTION → LOAD FICHE INTO RETRIEVAL UNIT → 3

3

RETRIEVAL MECHANISM → DISPLAY (OPTICAL)

DISC STORAGE → CENTRAL PROCESSING UNIT (MINI-COMPUTER)

KEYBOARD

ON-LINE CONTROL COMPUTER

QUERY/RETRIEVE/DISPLAY STATION
(One of several)

＊ Indicate number of duplicates made if more than one.

Fig. 2.6. A micrographic system utilizing fully automated, computer-aided retrieval of information by subject in a telephone company engineering operation. The system features an interactive minicomputer terminal through which the appropriate information is automatically retrieved from a mechanized microform store and displayed on a reader screen.

32

page images, any one of which can be brought to the viewing screen in a matter of seconds.

Besides guiding and controlling retrieval of data, the system software also controls updating when existing documents are voided or reissued and when new ones are added. Thus, when an engineer keys-in the number of the practice he wants to reference, he is assured of retrieving the latest issue.

In the normal situation, where the user does not know the specific documents he wants to reference, but only the general category of information, he can do one of two things to effect initial retrieval:
  (1) key-in only that portion of the document number representing the general category, an action which will retrieve and display a master numeric index of all documents in that category, or,
  (2) key-in the first few characters of a keyword through a keyword index, an action that will retrieve and display a title list.
In either case, once having narrowed the search via the displayed lists, the user need only key-in two additional digits to display the specific document. Thereafter, manipulation of appropriate buttons permits page-by-page "browsing" of the document, calling up a cross-referenced document, "marking" a page to which one may wish to return, producing a print, or doing any of several other things to aid in obtaining all the information needed. When reference to the last screen image is complete, the touch of a button returns the fiche to its storage slot and makes the system ready for the next inquiry.

Figure 2.6 depicts the system schematically.

* * *

The various representative systems described in this chapter illustrate the impressive scope of applications in which micrographics serve as a viable information storage and accessing tool. The next chapter will attempt to classify and define micrographic systems from various points of view.

* * *

Suggested Additional Reading

Badler, M.M., "Who Doesn't Use Microfilm?" *Information and Records Management,* March, 1975. p.38.
Bishop, Wiley L., "Micrographics in Records Management." *NMA Proceedings, 1974.* Silver Spring, Md.: NMA. pp.II-129—II-137.
Buchwald, Robert V., "Medical Records Storage and Retrieval." *NMA Proceedings, 1971.* Silver Spring, Md.: NMA. pp.II-28—II-35.
Cochran, Eugene R., "Dun and Bradstreet Uses Microfiche for Quick, Easy Access to Accounting Data." *The Journal of Micrographics,* January/February 1972. pp.137-140.
Darling, Pamela W., "Developing a Preservation Microfilming Program." *Library Journal,* November 1, 1974. pp.2803-2809.
Edgerton, Curtis, "The Mine Map Repository—A Source of Mine Map Data," *The Journal of Micrographics,* May/June 1975. pp.235-240.

Fricke, Charles L., "Micro Cataloging as Used by the Briggs & Stratton Corporation." *The Journal of Micrographics,* September/October 1974. pp.31-37.

Gaddy, Dale, *A Microform Handbook.* Silver Spring, Md.: NMA, 1974. 96p.

Harmon, Catherine B., "Microfilm in the Classroom," *NMA Proceedings, 1971.* Silver Spring, Md.: NMA. pp. II-25—II-27.

Hempel, Gardiner, "New Uses of Microfilm in Business." *NMA Proceedings, 1973.* Silver Spring, Md.: NMA. pp.II-266—II-275.

Levet, Wayne J., "Immediate Microfilming in Law Enforcement." *NMA Proceedings, 1974.* Silver Spring, Md.: NMA. pp. II-261—II-263.

Little, W. Douglas, "A University's Solution to Maintaining Student Records." *NMA Proceedings, 1974.* Silver Spring, Md.: NMA. pp.II-204—II-210.

"Microfiche Jacket System Solves Problem for State Government." *Reproduction Review and Methods,* May 1975. p.22.

"Microfilm Eases the Paper Crunch." *Information and Records Management,* March 1975. p.75.

"Microfilm Retrieval System Speeds Fingerprint ID for New York Police." *Computerworld,* September 26, 1973. p.50.

Miller, Lionel, "Micrographic Applications in the Federal Government." *The Journal of Micrographics,* September/October 1974. pp.3-8.

Moren, Bertil, and Kaj Ha:son Holmdahl, "Reduced Format X-rays—The Kalmar Method." *The Journal of Micrographics,* November/December 1973. pp.71-80.

Nanney, Thomas G., *Using Microfilm Effectively.* New York, N.Y.: Geyer-McAllister Publications, 1968. 121p.

Panorama. A quarterly publication of Eastman Kodak, describing various micrographic system case histories.

The Journal of Micrographics, January 1971: Special issue on the uses of micrographics in education. November/December 1971: Special micropublishing issue.

Torok, Stephen, "Microform Utilization in Europe—A Librarian's Observations." *The Journal of Micrographics,* May/June 1975. pp.215-222.

"Unoriginal Solutions to Microcopying Problems." Case history pamphlet by Scott Graphics, 1975.

Wolf, David R., "Case Studies," *NMA Proceedings, 1973.* Silver Spring, Md.: NMA. pp.II-60—II-82.

Chapter 3

Classification of Systems

Archival vs. Active • Manual vs. Automated • Reference vs. Reproduction • Unitized vs. Collective • Centralized vs. Decentralized

The previous chapter contained a glimpse of some of the ways in which micrographic systems may be classified or differentiated. The distinction was made, for example, between *archival* and *active* systems, and between *manual* and *automated* access to the file. This chapter will examine these in slightly more detail, and will look at three additional classifications: *reference* vs *reproduction, unitized* vs *collective* filing, and *centralized* vs *decentralized* operation.

Before proceeding, it should be clear that no system, regardless of size, can be classified in only one way; any micrographic system must, by nature, fit a combination of at least three of the above categories. For example, an archival file may be accessed either manually or automatically, but even if it is never accessed it must exist in unitized or collective and in centralized or decentralized form. It is even possible that a combination of *all* of the separate classifications will apply for a given system.

I. Archival vs Active

As indicated in the two preceding chapters, there are basically two kinds of archival micrographic systems. One functions merely to *retain* copies of original documents that have been destroyed as a space-saving move, and the other ensures the existence of a *duplicate* file in the event the original documents are inadvertently lost or destroyed.

In the first of these systems, retention of the documents in microform is usually just a matter of complying with certain legal requirements. (This will be explored further in Chapter 7). Chances are there will seldom, if ever, be any need to access that file other than to update and purge it occasionally. The second type of archival file is commonly known as a *disaster* file, and its existence generally assumes retention of the originals as well as the microforms, but in separate locations.

The typical disaster file is physically located in an environment that is insulated against fire, moisture and other potentially damaging phenomena. There are commercial warehousing operations that specialize in the provision of such facilities—some of them in man-made caves located underground or in mountains.

The word "active" as applied to files (paper *or* microfilm) may be deceiving in one respect, namely that a large archival file can be quite active from the standpoints of updating and purging. Nevertheless, the word is usually reserved to apply to files that are actively *accessed.* Such files might also be referred to as *dynamic* or *vital,* as opposed to archival or inactive—in other words, a file that is essential to one's normal business or professional activities.

Historically, it is probably safe to say that, until the early 1960s, microfilm was still predominantly an archival medium. That situation has since changed and the medium now ranks as one of the more dynamic and versatile tools in use within the information handling environment.

II. Manual vs Automated

It can be said with some validity that there is no such thing as a fully automated micrographic system. Theoretically, such a system would have to read the user's mind. But even if it is accepted that the manual keying of selection codes falls within the context of automation, most so-called fully automated systems still require at least a degree of manual purging and updating.

Conversely, it can be said that most modern manual systems are automated in some degree. For example, while we may have to manually select and insert a roll of film or a cartridge into a reader, the search for a specific image is often aided by a controllable speed electric motor. In fact, one of the first such units on the market was thought to be such a sophisticated advance that it was dubbed an "electronic" reader.

There are, of course, degrees of automation. The question is where to draw the lines that separate systems into *manual, semi-automated* and *automated* classifications. Throughout the remainder of this book, two general rules will apply with regard to the use of these three terms:

1. They will normally refer to the *retrieval* of information from a microform file, and not necessarily to the updating and purging of the file;
2. The following definitions will generally apply —
    (a) *Manual system:* any system in which the microform must be manually selected by some system of eye-readable indexing; manually inserted into the display or reproduction device; *and* the specific image located by a combination of manual and visual operations.
    (b) *Semi-automated system:* any system in which the keying-in of a retrieval code automatically retrieves a specific carrier (fiche, card, etc.) *or* specific image, but with human handling of the

microform being required at some point in the process.

(c) *Fully automated system:* any system in which the keying-in of a retrieval code automatically retrieves the microform *and* displays the desired image, and in which, after reference, the simple manipulation of a key will return the selected microform to file.

Automated retrieval will be covered in detail in the next chapter.

III. *Reference vs Reproduction*

In perhaps a majority of cases, the end use of a micrographic system is the viewing of a microimage on a reader screen. A system that offers no reproduction capability beyond this is a *reference* system.

There are many instances, however, where the viewing of a screen image is an intermediate step in the retrieval of documents from a microform file. In such instances, a user, having perhaps viewed a series of images, will select one or more of which duplicate microforms or enlarged paper prints will subsequently be requested. Although the word *reproduction* can apply to screen images, in micrographic-systems terminology it normally refers to the production of "hard copy"—paper prints of the enlarged micro-images—as opposed to "soft copy"—screen images. For the reproduction of microimages in kind—i.e., 1:1 (nonreduced, nonenlarged) reproduction on film, usually by contact printing—the word *duplication* is generally preferred. However, duplication may be considered a form of reproduction.

Reference to a microimage is not necessarily a prerequisite to reproduction. The user of the system may automatically request a duplicate or print based on the identifying code (drawing or document number) without first having viewed the filed microimage. But, more important from a systems planning point of view is the fact that there are micrographic applications where nothing beyond reference to a screen image is ever required, in which case no reproduction or duplication capability need be provided. Where the need for these added capabilities does exist, the cost of the system will be increased accordingly.

IV. *Unitized vs Collective*

As indicated in Chapter 1, the nature of the documents in a micrographic system will usually dictate the general class of microform on which the system will be based. The two general classes are *unitized* and, for want of a better term, *collective.*

Unitized generally refers to the confinement of one document—or one page of a multipage document—per unit carrier,* and *collective* implies that two or more documents, related or unrelated, are contained on the same unit carrier. We might cite as typical of the first class an aperture

---

*The term *unit carrier* is used here—and shall be used throughout the remainder of the book wherever necessary—to distinguish between a single unit of a particular microform and the name by which that type of microform is known. For example, an instruction to "select the applicable microform" could mean to choose a microfiche versus a cartridge, whereas an instruction to "select the applicable unit carrier" will make it clearer that a particular fiche should be selected from a collection of fiche or that a particular cartridge should be selected from a collection of cartridges.

card containing one frame of 35 millimeter microfilm. And we might cite as typical of the second class a 100-foot roll of 16 or 35 milimeter microfilm.

However, there are degrees of unitization. For example, a single *microfiche* sheet (or fiche unit carrier) containing all the pages of a given issue of a periodical—or a set of perhaps four fiche containing all the pages of a single book—would also qualify as a unitized microform. On the other hand, the same format microfiche containing images of many separate personnel records, related only in that the persons described are employed by the same firm, would, in that usage, be a collective microform. Conceivably, even the 35 mm aperture card could function as a collective microform by containing multiple, high-reduction document images within its single frame.

In summary, then, the distinction between unitized and collective is not so much one of the specific microform as it is one of application and the way in which the individual documents are grouped or separated within the file. Chapters 7 and 9 will cover the factors influencing the choice between the unitized and collective approaches in the planning of a micrographic system.

V. Centralized vs Decentralized

By nature, micrographic systems lend themselves to decentralized operation. Not only can the master microforms be readily duplicated on relatively inexpensive equipment, but the compactness of a microimage file, as compared with its paper equivalent, makes it feasible to have more than one file of the same material in scattered locations.

This can be a problem as well as an advantage. For example, in engineering offices served by a single master microform file of drawings and specifications, the engineers have a tendency to accumulate *satellite* files of duplicate microforms in their desk drawers. The practice is fine from the standpoint of convenience, but it tends to negate one of the other advantages of micrographic systems—namely the ease of updating and purging, and the consequent assurance that the file is always current. The engineer working from his own private file loses this assurance to the extent that he does not regularly check with the master file on the current status of the various documents.

We can perhaps best see the *advantage* of micrographics in this regard when the same situation exists on a larger scale—e.g., the duplication of master microforms in quantity at a central location for distribution to a number of *satellite master* files. Updating of these "second generation" (once-removed from the camera original) master files, which may be dispersed over a wide geographic area, is facilitated by the speed and ease with which new masters can be created, duplicated and distributed.

Of course, a microform file can also be strictly centralized in the same way as the typical paper file. In fact, the micrographic system, while lending itself to decentralized operation, also offers certain advantages over paper from the standpoint of strict *security*. For example, in a fully automated micrographic system designed strictly for *reference* (as opposed to reproduction or duplication), the file masters never fall into the user's hands in any form. They are available only in purely *visual* form as screen images, and, to the extent that an effective updating and purging program is maintained, the user is assured that the information he accesses is always that which is currently valid.

Taking this capability a step further, we can see how the compactness of microforms permits isolation of the mechanized master file in a location from which it is normally accessible only by closed-circuit TV or facsimile communication. (See Chapter 5.) Access can be from any number of authorized sites remote from the isolated central file. A system of this design not only further increases file security, but permits use of normally uninhabitable space for the file.

* * *

No doubt there are additional ways to classify micrographic systems, but these are the principal ones.

One of those discussed above, automated retrieval, will be covered in detail in the next chapter.

* * *

Suggested Additional Reading

Keane, Edward T., "A Microform for Active Records." *NMA Proceedings, 1973.* Silver Spring, Md.: NMA. pp.II-300—II-307.
Knowles, N. Douglas, "Unitized Systems in the Office Environment." *NMA Proceedings, 1973.* pp.II-307—II-311.
Leisinger, Albert H., *Microphotography for Archives.* Washington, D.C.: National Archives, 1968. 52p.
"Using Underground Vaults and Commercial Records Centers." *Information and Records Management,* February 1974. p.12.

Chapter 4
Search Aids and Automated Retrieval

*Retrieval Aids • Electronic Logic • Semiauto-
mated Systems • Fully Automated Systems •
Computer-Aided Retrieval*

From the moment microfilm evolved from an archival to an active information storage medium, it was inevitable that ways would be sought to
mechanically aid or automate the task of retrieving specific images from a
file. An early development in this direction was the use of visual location
markers on the film, appearing periodically on the screen of a roll film
reader as the film was advanced. This was followed by the equipping of
readers with odometers and motorized film advances. Eventually, automatic frame-finding by photoelectric sensing evolved.

Following is an overview of the various techniques in use in present-day
micrographic systems to aid or automate the retrieval of selected
microimages.

I. Retrieval Aids

Techniques that help an operator in the visual search for a specific item
in a microform file, but that do not automatically locate a specific microform or the desired microimage, should be regarded merely as retrieval
aids. There are several types, and, as will be seen, most are associated with
roll film system.

1. Visual Aids

There are basically two types of visual retrieval aids. One is the
odometer, which is an integral part of a reader, and the other the *on-
film indicator,* which is integral to the specific microform. Both are
applicable only to roll film readers.

The only link the odometer has with the microform content is the

41

index of image addresses associated with a particular roll. It is actually a film length indicator, no different from those found on some movie cameras and tape recorders. The index may exist separately or as a microimage at the beginning of the roll. The reading on the odometer is merely an approximation of the indexed address. When the desired number is reached, the operator stops the rapid advance and *browses,* in one direction or the other, to locate the specific image being sought.

The on-film indicator, sometimes referred to as *visual indexing,* may take one of several forms, of which the following two are most common:

(a) *flash targets*—a conspicuously contrasting gap between batches of documents, appearing as a flash on the screen as the film advances rapidly through the reader. The flashes serve as location indicators while in motion, and, when stopped on the screen, may contain identifying information on the batch of images that follows;

(b) *code lines*—lines recorded in the spaces between document images and lying parallel with the length axis of the film. When the film is rapidly advancing, the line segments tend to join together and appear continuous. The identity of an image or batch of images is indicated by the position of the line along the axis perpendicular to the film length (normally the vertical axis with respect to the screen). Numbers printed on a fixed scale beside the screen match up with the code lines and provide a numeric reading of the location address at any point during film advance. The code line method is illustrated in Figure 4.1.

Code Lines

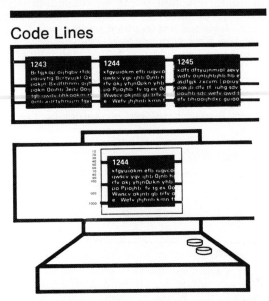

Fig. 4.1. Code line method of indexing roll microforms. Horizontal lines recorded on the film serve as shifting indexing marks to help locate document images via a fixed scale mounted vertically beside the reader screen.

Fig. 4.2. "Pantograph" type frame locator on a microfiche reader. With the fiche placed properly in the carriage, the pointer is manually moved to the desired frame on the grid replica, and that frame of the actual fiche will appear on the screen.

2. *Motorized Advance*

Substitution of an electric motor drive for the manual "crank" on a roll film reader is another retrieval aid, and one that is often used in conjunction with one or another of the visual aids just described. In its simplest form, the motorized advance is under direct manual control via a simple switch, usually having variable speed settings. In a more sophisticated arrangement, a set of pushbuttons and associated simple logic are provided to advance the film in discrete lengths, automatically stopping it somewhere close to the desired frame.

3. *"Pantograph"*

Most fiche readers are equipped with an image-finding mechanism somewhat resembling a *pantograph* (a device that reproduces manual movements, usually for the purpose of copying graphic designs). It is similar to a pantograph in the sense that a manual action at point A produces a like action at point B. Specifically, in the fiche reader, a manually shiftable pointer is moved to the desired frame on a replica of the fiche grid, and through a mechanical linkage with the microform carriage, causes the corresponding frame on the actual fiche to be moved into view on the reader screen. See Figure 4.2.

II. Electronic Logic

Automated locating of a specific image on a microform requires a combination of electronic logic, like that used in a pocket calculator, and a precision high-speed advancing mechanism capable of rapid acceleration and sudden stops. Where the locating scheme involves optical codes recorded on the microform, photoelectric sensing is an additional requirement.

1. Nonoptical Retrieval

An example of a nonoptical retrieval scheme is that used in some fully automated fiche systems where the grid format is rigidly standardized, (a fairly normal requirement for modern fiche systems). The first few digits of the keyed-in retrieval code select the fiche containing the desired image and free it for automatic insertion into the image plane of the reader's optical system. The next segment of the code causes the fiche to be moved the correct number of positions along one coordinate, and the last segment causes it to be moved the correct number along the other coordinate. The selected image is then displayed on the screen.

In a simpler configuration of essentially the same retrieval mechanism, a fiche may be manually inserted in a slot on a reader, and the desired frame brought to the screen by pushbutton selection.

2. Optical Retrieval

There are basically two varieties of optical retrieval, and both are normally applied to roll film systems:

(a) *image-("blip") count*—during film advance, the photosensing circuitry counts image frames by counting optical marks, called "blips," associated with the frames. When the right count has been reached in accordance with the manually input address code, the film advance is suddenly stopped and the selected image is displayed on the screen.

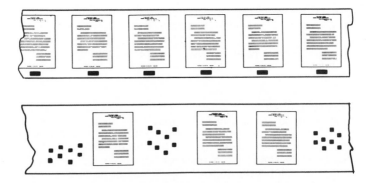

Fig. 4.3 "Blip" (top) and binary optical (bot.) retrieval coding on roll film. The blip merely permits automatic frame counting by optical sensing. The binary code contains discrete information about the associated image or images.

(b) *binary code*—the photosensor consists of multiple sensing elements, one for each of the optical marks representing a discrete binary code associated with each image or group of related images on the film. The sensors permit the film advance to continue until the sensed code matches the one input at the manual keyboard, thereupon halting the advance and displaying the selected image on the screen.

Figure 4.3 illustrates the distinction between blip and binary optical coding on the film.

III. Semi-Automated Systems

As noted in the preceding chapter, a semiautomated micrographic system is one that automatically retrieves a specific carrier (fiche, card, etc.) *or* specific image, but requires human handling of the microform at some point in the process. There are two basic system configurations that meet this description:

1. Manual insert/keyed search

In this configuration, the operator visually selects the correct carrier (typically a roll or cartridge) from the file, manually inserts it into the automated reader, and then keys in an address code representing the document being sought. The logic-controlled search mechanism in the reader thereupon rapidly advances the film to the desired image and stops it so that the image is displayed, properly centered and focused, on the viewing screen. (See Figure 4.4.)

2. Keyed search/manual insert

In this configuration, the operator keys in a retrieval code representing pertinent descriptive information, and a logic-controlled search mechanism thereupon physically "liberates" one or more microimage carriers (normally fiche or aperture cards) from a mechanized random file. Selection is by an automated variation of the *McBee Keysort* System, and "liberation" of the selected carriers may be by any of a variety of mechanical means of causing them to stand out from the rest of the file. The operator then manually extracts the liberated carriers and views them in a conventional reader. A view of a typical mechanized file of this system configuration is shown in Figure 4.5.

IV. Fully Automated Systems

Fully automated systems—those that automatically retrieve a specific carrier from an integral file *and* locate and display a specific image—vary widely in design. There are fully automated systems designed around each of the standard microforms, as well as some nonstandard ones. But, of the total population, microfiche tends to dominate because it lends itself best to integral storage and complete file-to-screen automation.

As compared with semiautomation, the principal advantage of a fully automated system is that it affords somewhat greater file security. Depending on the system and how it is used, it *may or may not* significantly improve retrieval time.

Fig. 4.4. "Manual insert/keyed search" type of semiautomated microform retrieval system. The selected microform is manually inserted in an automated reader. The keying-in of a retrieval code then automatically locates and displays the specific frame being sought.

Fig. 4.5. "Keyed search/manual insert" type of semiautomated retrieval system. Keying-in a retrieval code causes one or more microimage carriers (cards or fiche) to be "liberated" from the mechanized file for manual extraction. After use, the removed carriers can be randomly refiled.

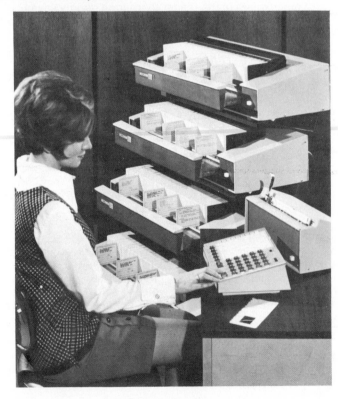

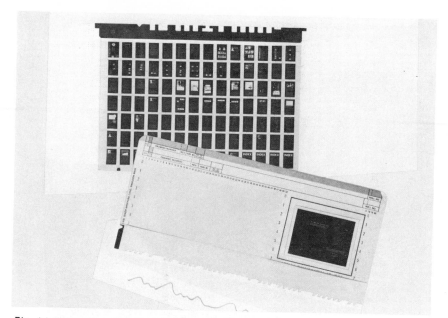

Fig. 4.6. Examples of "edge-notching" of microforms for automated retrieval purposes. In the upper example, a separate metal clip affixed to the fiche contains the notch coding. In the lower example, the notches are cut directly into the card, along its bottom edge.

1. Fiche Systems

In the typical fiche system, each fiche is binary coded prior to its entry into the mechanized file. The code may take one of several forms, but *edge-notching* is the most popular. One reason is that the notches can be cut in the fiche (usually along the bottom edge) with relative ease on an inexpensive apparatus. Alternatively, an add-on clip or jacket of some sort may contain the notches, and the fiche itself need not be altered. Either way, an additional reason for the popularity of edge-notching is that the code need not be predetermined at the time of filming, as would be the case with optical coding, and existing fiche may be encoded.

A third and very important reason is that edge-notching permits use of what amounts to a mechanized version of the *McBee Keysort* System: selection of one fiche from among many while all remain relatively stationary in their storage bins. The system has the added advantage of permitting random filing: the individual fiche need not necessarily be returned to the same spot in the file from which it came. An example of edge-notching is shown in Figure 4.6.

Having been "liberated" from the file, the selected fiche is mechanically inserted into position at the optical system's film plane, mechanically moved a discrete distance along the two coordinates (this also in accordance with the keyed-in retrieval code), "clamped" in place, and probably automatically focused. The selected image thereupon appears on the reader screen, the entire process having taken perhaps 3 seconds.

Figure 4.7 shows a typical, self-contained, fully automated desktop fiche retrieval unit.

47

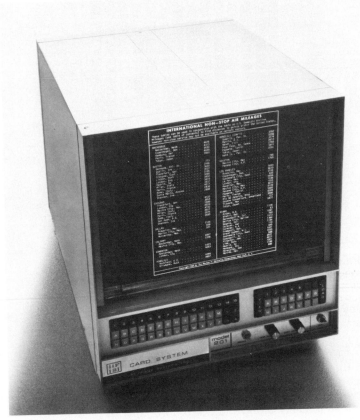

Fig. 4.7. A typical, fully automated desktop retrieval/display unit. Contained within it is a microfiche file of some 750,000 page images.

2. Roll Film Systems

Although it may be a more cumbersome task for a mechanism to automatically select a specific roll of film (reel, cartridge or cassette) from among many, as compared with fiche, the search for an image on a roll is simpler since it involves only one axis of movement. For this reason, roll film lends itself best to automated retrieval when the complete file can be confined to a single roll. An example of an application where this criterion is met is retrieval of the microimaged pages of a telephone directory. At least one such retrieval system is in use in a telephone company directory assistance operation, the individual pages being retrieved at high speed with the aid of discrete optical codes recorded along one edge of the film.

There is also at least one commercial system, fully automated, in which roll film cartridges of special design are automatically selected and conveyed to a loading port, automatically inserted into the reader mechanism and scanned, and the desired image automatically retrieved and displayed. On completion of reference, the press of a button automatically rewinds the cartridge and returns it to its proper place in the mechanized file.

A self-contained, fully automated, commercial roll film retrieval system is pictured in Figure 4.8.

Fig. 4.8. A self-contained, fully automated, commercial roll film retrieval system.

3. Aperture Card Systems

Fully automated retrieval systems for E.A.M. microfilm cards have somehow failed, thus far, to stimulate much interest among users of this microform. One reason may be that the "unit" nature of the aperture card—the fact that each card normally bears only a single image, or, at best, a very small number of multiple images—means that, to be practical, a system would have to be designed to accommodate a relatively large number of cards. This, in turn, means that not only would the system tend to be physically large, but the mechanized selection process may have to be somewhat more intricate than for a fiche or roll system.

Another drawback is that, although each card already contains a discrete identifying code in the form of keypunching, it would be difficult to design a retrieval system around the use of this keypunched information. In the systems developed to date, the keypunching has had to be converted to some other form of coding, such as edge-notching, before the cards are added to the mechanized file. In some cases, this may mean having to involve a computer in the system to enable keying-in of the actual document identification code, and having it automatically translated to the special retrieval code for that document.

4. *Mixed and Nonstandard Microforms*

Besides those designed around a given standard microform, fully automated systems have been offered in which mixtures of cards, chips and fiche are retrievable. The interfiling is made possible by containing the microforms within transparent plastic carriers of uniform design. The carriers, rather than the individual microforms, contain the special encoding that permits their automated selection from the mechanized file in response to keyed-in retrieval codes.

Fig. 4.9. A selection of retrieval-coded chips and strips. These are nonstandard microforms specially tailored to facilitate automated retrieval.

In addition, there are systems built around nonstandard microforms such as high storage density fiche ("ultrafiche"), "chips," and "scrolls." One ultrafiche system currently available is capable of internally storing 120,000 document images in a single cartridge not much bigger than an eyeglass case. Any one of these thousands of tiny images can be automatically retrieved and displayed on the built-in viewing screen within 3 seconds of the keying-in of a retrieval code. A selection of retrieval-coded chips and strips is shown in Figure 4.9.

5. *Remote Access Systems*

There are instances where it may be desirable to access a file remotely from other locations, as in the case of an underground

50

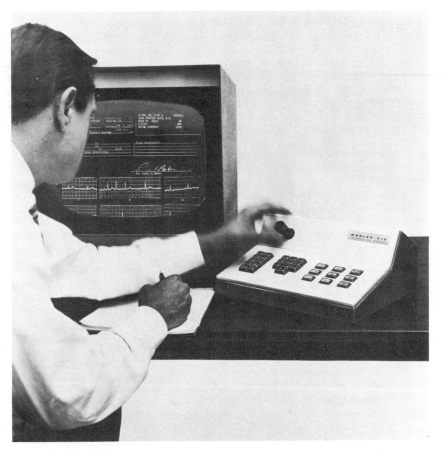

Fig. 4.10. A CCTV terminal for remote retrieval and viewing of microimages electronically. The "joy stick," for which the user is seen reaching, permits the distant camera to be remotely controlled (positioning of images, "zooming," etc.) from the receive terminal.

security vault containing documents to which reference may be needed in an office some distance away. Nothing could be better in that kind of situation than a fully automated micrographics system. The fact that microforms lend themselves so readily to automated retrieval is one reason. Another is that the electrical impulses that initiate the retrieval cycle via a local keyboard can just (or almost) as easily reach the retrieval mainframe via communication lines from another location.

The question is, how does the retrieved document image get from the mainframe to the remote point? The answer is *closed-circuit TV* or *facsimile.* Suffice it to say, for the moment, that both are graphic transmission systems, differing from one another chiefly in cost and speed of transmission. These technologies will be discussed in greater detail in the next chapter. Figure 4.10 shows one kind of remote access retrieval configuration.

51

V. Computer-Aided Retrieval

All semi- or fully automated micrographic retrieval systems require some form of integral electronic logic that amounts to a built-in basic minicomputer, dedicated to a specific task. However, the term *computer-aided retrieval* is usually reserved to apply to the combining of micrographic and interactive computer terminals in a way that permits the user to retrieve microfilmed *information,* as differentiated from specific documents. The computer used may be either time-shared or dedicated. This decision will usually depend on the size and level of activity of the system.

The reader will recall that such a system was briefly described in Chapter 2 as an example of a relatively complex micrographic system configuration. Now let's examine a similar one, but with the aim of seeing how the separate resources of the computer and the microform file come together at the accessing terminal. In this example, the function of the system is to automate the retrieval of information from a newspaper "morgue" (clipping file). Here are the progressive steps by which the desired information might be obtained:

(1) the user enters, via the keyboard of the computer terminal, the keyword or name of the subject on which information is being sought;

(2) the teleprinter portion of the computer terminal responds by printing out a subject breakdown—i.e., it divides the subject into various keyword categories, or dates or whatever happens to be appropriate for the particular subject, along with numbers indicating the quantity of separate items filed in each category;

(3) the user considers the list and then enters on the keyboard the appropriate code language (perhaps the first three letters of the keyword) to retrieve each item of interest. If all items are desired, perhaps the word "ALL" is keyed-in;

(4) the computer pulses the retrieval logic in the micrographics terminal to access the first of the requested list of items. It is retrieved from the terminal's integral microimage store and displayed on the screen;

(5) having perused this first item, the user keys the computer to go to the next one in succession, or to print the first item (assuming the micrographics terminal has a print capability), and *then* go onto the next one, and so on;

(6) when the search has been satisfied, the user makes the appropriate control manipulation(s) to return the system to its "off" or standby state. Where a remote time-shared computer is being accessed, this may consist of hanging up a phone.

In a well-planned system, the operating instructions will be made conveniently available to the user, possibly as a series of messages printed out by the teleprinter at each step.

From the standpoint of the micrographics portion of the total terminal configuration, a computer-aided system may be semi- or fully automated, or even manual for that matter. The foregoing illustration describes a fully automated configuration. In a semi-automated or manual configuration, the computer, instead of directly pulsing a retrieval mechanism, might simply indicate (via teleprinter, CRT, etc.) one or more numbers identifying

52

specific microforms to be manually retrieved by the user and inserted in a reader.

It is interesting that, even in the fully automated configuration, the normally dominant computer is relegated to serving the micrographic system in a peripheral capacity, functioning, in effect, as an automated index.

The terminal of a typical computer-aided micrographic system is shown in figure 4.11.

Fig. 4.11. A typical terminal configuration for a computer-aided micrographic retrieval system.

* * *

The next chapter will deal with ancillary technologies; i.e. other technologies that somehow complement micrographics, the application of which can effectively broaden the scope of capabilities of a micrographics system.

Suggested Additional Reading

Bloom, Leon, "Information Retrieval Using Micrographics," *The Journal of Micrographics,* November/December 1974. pp.55-62.

Courtot, Marilyn E., *Microform Indexing and Retrieval Systems.* Silver Spring, Md.: NMA, 1975. 24p.

Exelbert, Rodd S., and Mitchell M. Badler, "Automatic Information Retrieval." *Information and Records Management,* February 1974. p.23.

Kish, Joseph L., Jr., "Microfilm Indexing Systems." *Business Graphics,* December 1974. p.30.

Merwin, Roy L., "Approaches to Automation of Business and Scientific Records and Information." *The Journal of Micrographics,* March/April 1972. pp.201-203.

Tauber, Alfred S., and Howard W. Hoadley, *Automatic Document Storage and Retrieval—A Market Emerges.* White Plains, N.Y.: Knowledge Industry Publications, Inc., 1973. 181p.

Teplitz, Arthur A., "Computer-Controlled Retrieval: A Primer." *The Journal of Micrographics,* September/October 1971. p.35.

"Using Underground Vaults and Commercial Records Centers." *Information and Records Management,* February 1974. p.12.

Chapter 5
Ancillary Technologies

COM • CIM • EAM Handling • Computer-Aided
Retrieval • Electronic Graphic Transfer

The title of this chapter may be a trifle deceiving in the sense that *ancillary* suggests an *adjunct* or *accessory.* The evolution of micrographics has been such that some of these "side" technologies that were once viewed merely as accessories have come to be accepted as intrinsic aspects of the micrographics concept. It is interesting and, to an extent, probably indicative of a continuing trend, that more than half the items covered in the chapter have a common bond in computer technology. To the extent that it has already happened, the marriage of micrographics to the computer was inevitable in view of the way the two technologies tend to complement each other. Computer Output Microfilming (COM) is a good example.

I. COM

Computer Output Microfilming* was introduced in the late 1950s as a high-speed alternative to impact printing on paper. It substitutes microfilm for paper and is particularly applicable to situations requiring large-volume print-out that is frequently updated and widely distributed. Present COM devices can produce document pages, or pages of data, at ten times the speed of line printers.

Among the earliest commercial COM devices were the 4000 series machines produced by Stromberg-Carlson, a long-established manufacturer of telephone and radio apparatus. At the heart of these units was a device called a *Charactron** * tube, a special cathode-ray tube (CRT) that had previously been developed by Convair for the Department of Defense. The *Charactron* tube contains a beam-shaping element that causes a charac-

---

*The M in COM can stand for Micro*film,* Micro*filming,* or Micro*filmer,* depending on the context in which the term is used.

**Charactron® is a registered trademark of Stromberg-DatagraphiX, Inc.

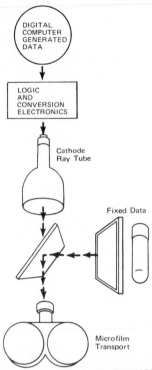

DIGITAL COMPUTER GENERATED DATA

LOGIC AND CONVERSION ELECTRONICS

Cathode Ray Tube

Fixed Data

Microfilm Transport

Cathode Ray Tube (CRT) Recording

ter or symbol to be formed on the screen in accordance with the position to which the electron beam was electrostatically deflected as it passed through the shaping element. A separate deflection circuit positions the character at the right place on the screen. The idea is to combine this special CRT with a microfilm camera head in such a way that the images produced on the tube's face by its electron beam are captured by the camera within a film frame, and then the film is automatically advanced to be ready to capture the next image. The CRT circuitry is designed to permit control of image creation by an external computer, thus permitting creation of microimages *by a computer* from input raw data. The basic concept is shown in Figure 5.1.

Fig. 5.1 Basic COM concept. The input is digital data from a magnetic tape or direct from a computer. This binary data is electronically processed into the form necessary to control an imaging device (in this case a cathode ray tube). A more or less conventional microfilm camera films the electronically formed light images, along with any fixed optical imagery that may be required.

COM caught on slowly at first, and then more rapidly as system planners began to recognize its potential. Additional manufacturers began to offer COM devices, and, in the ensuing competition, new and enhanced capabilities and flexibilities began to emerge, with the result that COM became increasingly viable as a computer peripheral. By about 1970 it was clear that, through COM, an inseverable bond had been established between the computer and micrographic technologies.

Modern COM devices offer various capabilities. Some are capable of only alphanumeric imaging, whereas others can function effectively as "plotters," creating infinite combinations of angles and curvatures to form intricate images on the CRT screen*—images that are permanently recorded on film *as they are formed*. Virtually all COMs have provision for *forms overlay*, which means that the computer-generated data can be mixed with

---

*There is no rule dictating that the imaging element of a COM device be a CRT. Among other approaches currently employed in commercial COM devices are the use of light-emitting diodes (LEDs), lasers, and direct electron beam techniques.

fixed-format printing within the same frame via optically superimposed slides; most are able to record some form of retrieval coding on the film; and most permit use of more than one film width.

COM devices can operate either *on-line* or *off-line* with regard to the computer mainframe. But, in either case, the images "created" on the film are a function of the computer software. The COM also usually has its own built-in logic which converts the input data to a form in which it can control the various functions—e.g., electron beam deflection and film advance.

Figure 5.2 shows the physical configurations of a selection of commercial COM units, and Figure 5.3 shows several examples of COM-produced images.

Fig. 5.2. A selection of commercially available COM devices. The typical unit costs about $100,000 to purchase or rents for about $3500 a month.

II. CIM

Computer *Input* Microfilm (CIM) is literally COM in reverse. A CIM device has microimages as its input and digital data as its output. Its usual purpose is to convert the visual microimages to magnetically recorded electrical pulses, a form in which they can be revised or otherwise manipulated under computer control. The altered magnetic "image" can then be fed to a COM device for output of a revised version of the original microimage.

Basically, here is how CIM works: on being input, the original microimage is scanned by a pin-point of light—the source may be a laser—in much the same manner that a TV camera dissects its subject into a serial stream of light variations. These variations are, in turn, converted to an electrical analog which, in TV terminology, would be called a "picture signal." Once in this form, it can easily be "digitized" and recorded on magnetic tape or discs to facilitate "editing" by precision deletion and addition of signal pulses as required. The exact nature of the alterations will depend on the system software and the manner in which manual controls are manipulated by a trained operator or engineer.

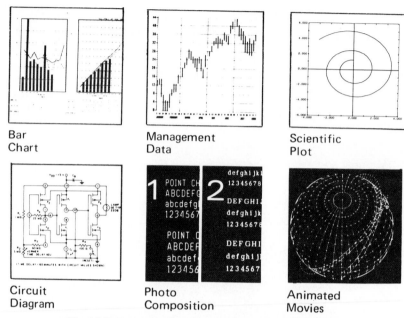

Bar
Chart

Management
Data

Scientific
Plot

Circuit
Diagram

Photo
Composition

Animated
Movies

Fig. 5.3 Some examples of COM-produced microimages.

Fig. 5.4. The "works" of a typical CIM device. A card-mounted microimage is scanned by a laser beam and converted to electronic digital data.

58

Figure 5.4 shows the laser scanner in a commercial CIM device, and Figure 5.5 shows actual "before-and-after" reproductions of a microimage that has gone the full CIM-COM route.

A CIM device can also function simply as a converter, to put microimages into digital storage (perhaps to be combined somehow with other data), or possibly to enable electronic transmission of the images via communication circuits. Moreover, with the CIM device available as a converter, it becomes possible to use microfilm, rather than magnetic tape, as the long-term retention medium for digital data. Microfilm has proved itself a very durable information storage medium—and an economical one. The same number of characters that might cost several dollars to store on magnetic discs can be stored on microform for a one-time cost of a few cents.

III. EAM Handling

One microform, the EAM aperture card, permits use of standard or slightly modified tab card-handling machines for keypunching, interpreting and high-speed sorting. These capabilities can be applied in the initial production of the microfilm cards, and in their duplication and distribution as well. Their use generally assumes a comparatively large operation in which great volumes of cards are produced and distributed on a fairly steady basis. Let's look at a typical example:

In the Bell Telephone System, all standard engineering drawings are on 35mm microfilm mounted in aperture cards. While drawing sheets are being filmed on planetary cameras, raw aperture cards are being keypunched and interpreted in the same order that the drawing images will appear on the processed film. Roll film and cards converge at the mounting station, where the individual frames are viewed, their identifying numbers compared with the interpreted data on the card, and the film is automatically cut and mounted. From each of several producing locations, the complete microfilm image cards are then mailed to a reproduction/distribution center where each original silver-halide microimage is contact-duplicated on diazo copy film premounted in apertured tab cards ("copy cards"). The duplicating is done automatically, at high speeds, and in quantities determined by computer-controlled distribution lists. In the process, the keypunching is reproduced from master to copy card to enable high-speed sorting for purposes of selective distribution.

As of this writing, the natural adaptability of EAM microfilm cards to machine sorting has been applied primarily in production and distribution, and has been virtually ignored in the area of automated document retrieval. The chief reason for this is that card selection by Hollerith keypunch sensing usually requires that the cards be in motion. Of course, this is also the case with selection by optical coding of images on microfilm reels. But, in a moving search, separate images on a common base (as in roll film) offer an obvious advantage over separate microform carriers. For aperture cards and microfiche, some form of edge-coding is generally preferred for automated retrieval because it permits one card or fiche sheet to be selected from among many while remaining relatively stationary within a file.

IV. Computer-Aided Retrieval

This modern adjunct to micrographic systems has already been dis-

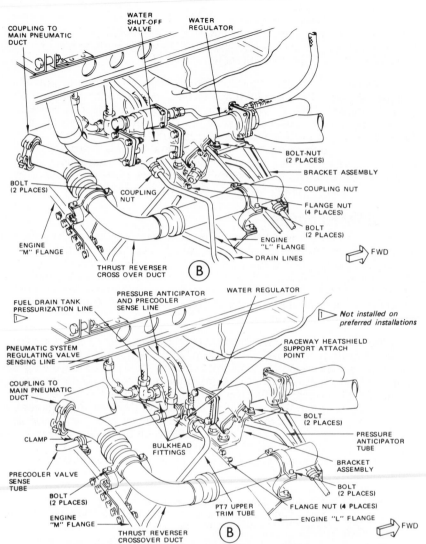

Fig. 5.5 Actual reproductions of microimages representing the input (left) and output (right) of an electronic editing system. The input image was converted to digital data by a CIM device; the data was electronically altered and then input to a COM device. The image on the right (except for the revision call-outs) is the resulting COM output.

cussed in Chapters 2 and 4. All that need be said further at this point is that, like COM, computer-assisted retrieval has come into such wide use in recent years that it is becoming more an aspect of the whole micrographics concept than an ancillary technology.

V. Electronic Graphic Transfer

We have seen how micrographics facilitates the retrieval of specific information from an extensive file. But what about *information transfer*—getting the retrieved information to where it is needed in situations where a central file may have to be accessed by persons geographically remote from it?

There are basically four ways to accomplish this electronically:

1. *Digital data*

Normally, the use of digital data communications in a micrographics environment implies two things—(1) that the filed information is in the form of alphanumerics, with perhaps some limited use of common symbols, and (2) that, for transmission, the information must be visually/manually translated to electrical pulses by a human operator at a keyboard. There are, of course, exceptions to this, one of them being *Optical Character Recognition (OCR)*. But, in the present state of the art, OCR is a comparatively complex and expensive proposition.

Another exception is the conversion of the output of an image scanner to a compacted digital data format. This will be covered in the discussion of *facsimile* that follows.

In terms of economics, basic digital data transfer, where the information is in a form that can be transmitted in standard "keyed-in" codes via narrow band circuits, incurs about the lowest transmission costs of any electronic transfer approach likely to be considered. (The economics of electronic transfer will be further covered in Chapter 8.)

2. *Facsimile*

The best way to understand facsimile communication—or *"fax,"* as it is often called—is to think of it as a kind of slowed-down TV. Besides speed, two other ways in which it differs from TV are that (1) the transmitting "Camera" is designed to view documents rather than "scenes," and (2) the output is "hard" rather than "soft"—i.e., tangible paper or film copy as opposed to an image on a CRT. A fax system is, in essence, an office copier with the input and output ends geographically separated. Hence the names *Telecopier** and *Remotecopier** for two of the more popular commercial systems.

In some maximum security and disaster files, where the actual file is deliberately isolated to prevent easy access or accidental loss, conventional paper-to-paper fax systems are used for controlled remote access. The send and receive stations of such systems are usually interconnected via the telephone dial network, and the control is in the form of human exchange of "passwords" or other pertinent identifying information prior to transmission. The caller, having suitably identified both himself and the document (or documents) he wants to access, waits for a "ready" indication, and then makes whatever simple manipulation is required to switch from the voice to the fax mode—possibly just insertion of the phone handset into an acoustic coupler.

With a conventional analog fax system, it takes anywhere from two to six minutes to receive each full, letter-size document transmitted. With the

---

*Telecopier® is a registered trademark of Xerox Corporation and Remotecopier® is a registered trademark of the 3M Company.

more expensive digital fax systems recently introduced, the transmission time for the same document is reduced to several seconds. These latter systems use special *redundancy reduction* technology to compact or "compress" the transmitter output (in effect programming the scanner to skip the blank portions of the document) and reformat it to a stream of binary code words not unlike the output of a teletypewriter. Such systems naturally cost more than their analog counterparts, and will therefore normally prove cost-effective only in situations where documents are exchanged at a comparatively high volume.

The fact that the conventional commercial fax system is a paper-to-paper system imposes an additional step in the transfer of information from a remote microform file, namely the conversion of the requested microimage to an enlarged paper copy prior to transmission. The logical question is, would it not make more sense to have a system that would accept a microform as its input? The answer is yes, and, in fact, such systems—generally referred to as *microfacsimile* systems—have been developed and are available. But, because of the present low demand, they are generally treated as custom equipment and are therefore costly.

Technically, there are no special problems in designing a fax system for microfilm input. Conventional optical scanning can be used in one of two ways:

(a) *scanning of an optically enlarged, projected image of the microimage.* Scanning would be by a moving aperture and, with the exception of the projection optics and a more intense light source, would require a design practically identical to that already in use in some paper scanning systems.

(b) *optical reduction of the scan spot and scanning area to permit direct scanning of the microimage at a scan resolution roughly equivalent to that which would be normal in scanning the original document directly.*

Obviously both of these approaches would inflict slight losses in resolution attributable to the added optics. The alternative would be to scan the microimage directly with a laser beam. At least one such microfacsimile scanner has already been developed.

Microform *output* from a fax receiver is also well within the realm of feasibility, and has, in fact, been successfully demonstrated in the laboratory. One of the more noteworthy developments in this direction is a unique system demonstrated by Bell Telephone Labs in which the received microimage is recorded by laser "machining" of microscopic holes in the surface of special film containing a thin metal coating. The recorded images are high resolution, permanent, and need no further processing.

Apart from this novel approach, it is also possible, with special programming, to use an existing, high resolution graphic COM device as a microfacsimile receiver. It could be used on a time-shared, store-and-forward basis, the incoming signals being stored on magnetic tape for delayed input to the COM unit during idle periods (overnight, for example).

Figure 5.6 shows a conventional, paper-to-paper, phone-coupled fax transceiver, and Figure 5.7 shows two commercially-available microfacsimile transmitters.

3. Closed-circuit TV

There are basically two problems with the use of closed-circuit TV (*CCTV*) in the remote accessing of document files. One is that higher resolutions are required than are normal for television transmission—e.g., 1000 scan lines per frame, as opposed to 525 for commercial TV—and the other is that, partly because of the high resolution requirement, an especially wide transmission bandwidth is required (in the neighborhood of 5 to 10 megahertz) and, consequently, transmission between geographically separated points is costly. For these reasons, whatever use is made of CCTV for remote document accessing is generally confined to in-house applications or to very restricted geographic areas.

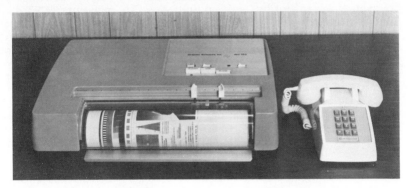

Fig. 5.6. A conventional desk-top fax transceiver, capable of sending or receiving a letter-size document in three to six minutes via telephone, over virtually unlimited geographical distances.

Fig. 5.7. Two "microfacsimile" transmitters. The one on the right is for aperture cards, and the one of the left transmits images from 16mm roll film cartridges.

CCTV does, however, also have two very important advantages in the remote accessing of files. One is that transmission is effectively instantaneous, and the other is its *zoom* capability. The latter is useful in compensating for inadequate resolution by its ability to zero-in on details of a document occupying the screen. In most CCTV systems designed for document retrieval applications, the zoom capability is remotely controllable from the receiving terminal.

4. *Slow-scan TV*

Slow scan TV (*SSTV*) utilizes standard TV apparatus for picture transmission via ordinary telephone lines at fax speeds. It would, in fact, qualify as a fax system except for its "soft" output—i.e., an image on a CRT screen. Special storage type CRTs are used in SSTV receivers to enable the slow-building image to be retained in its entirety for viewing. If a conventional CRT were used, all the viewer would observe would be a laterally oscillating spot of light slowly advancing from the top to the bottom of the screen. The screen would be as blank at the end of transmission as it was at the start.

With the addition of a print capability at the receiver—e.g., a Polaroid camera attachment for the CRT—an SSTV system could conceivably function as a fax system. But it would tend to be a crude substitute. The one ad-

Fig. 5.8. A central station for semiautomated remote retrieval of microimages via facsimile communication. In response to a telephoned request, the operator keys in the document identifier to retrieve the image of it on the reader screen. By scanning, the image is converted to an electrical analog, which can be transmitted "real time" via communication circuits, or magnetically recorded for delayed transmission, possibly at a lower speed.

vantage it would have in this respect is that a comparatively inexpensive microfacsimile transmitter could be had simply by use of an appropriate close-up lens on a relatively inexpensive TV camera. SSTV is also a *potentially* practical alternative to fax in a situation where documents in the remote file need only be temporarily referenced and where copies are never required. How practical it would actually be in a given situation would depend somewhat on output resolution requirements.

Perhaps the ultimate in micrographic systems—to the extent that it can be proved feasible—would be a central master file remotely accessible via fax or TV from any number of stations, simply by keying-in appropriate codes on a compact retrieval/display console. Such systems have, in fact, been designed and implemented, but primarily on an experimental basis. One configuration of a central transmitting station is shown in Figure 5.8.

Whatever the ancillary technologies that are applied, and in whatever configurations and combinations, the significant thing about micrographics that should be evident in what has been said of it so far in this book is its inherent flexibility—the fact that it can be as simple or complex, or can be applied on as small or large a scale as is required to satisfy the users' needs.

* * *

The next chapter will briefly examine the extent to which micrographics is covered by standards, and will identify the active standards organizations.

Suggested Additional Reading

Airhart, Truett, "Computer Output Microfilm: A Powerful System Tool." *The Journal of Micrographics,* January/February 1974. pp.99-105.
Avedon, Don M., *Computer Output Microfilm.* 2nd. edition. Silver Spring, Md.: NMA, 1971. 232p.
Carroll, H.L., "Use of Microfilm Aperture Cards in IBM Equipment." *NMA Proceedings, 1960.* Silver Spring, Md.: NMA. pp118-122.
    (Author's note: Though old, this remains a good basic description of the machine-handling of microfilm aperture cards).
Clarke, Alfred L., "ABC's of COM." *The Journal of Micrographics,* March/April 1972. pp.205-206.
Computer Handling of Graphical Information. Washington, D.C.: Society of Photographic Scientists and Engineers, 1970. 278p.
Costigan, Daniel M., *FAX: The Principles and Practice of Facsimile Communication.* Philadelphia, Pa.: Chilton Book Co., 1971. 270p.
Costigan, Daniel M., "Microfacsimile: A Status Report." *The Journal of Micrographics,* May/June 1971. pp.189-199.
Fundamentals of Computer Output Microfilm. Silver Spring, Md.: NMA, 1974. 24p.
Gray, S.B., "Aspects of the Computer-Microfilm Interface." *NMA Proceedings, 1968.* Silver Spring, Md.: NMA. pp.87-92.

Griffin, John M., "On-Line Microfilm." *NMA Proceedings, 1972.* Silver Spring, Md.: NMA. pp.III-70—III-77.

Hilton, Howard J., "CATV and Microforms." *NMA Proceedings, 1968.* Silver Spring, Md.: NMA. pp.26-39.

Jackson, B.F., and others, "AMACUS II." *NMA Proceedings, 1968.* Silver Spring, Md.: NMA. pp.93-105.

Knudson, Donald R., and Richard S. Marcus, "The Design of a Microimage Storage and Transmission Capability Into an Integrated Information Transfer System." *The Journal of Micrographics,* September/October 1972. pp.15-20.

Mallender, Ian H., "Digital Methods of Microfilm Communication." *The Journal of Micrographics,* Fall, 1969. pp.20-23, 26-45.

Preisser, Walter J., "Computer Input Microfilm (CIM)." *NMA Proceedings, 1972.* Silver Spring, Md.: NMA. pp.II-112—II-114.

Schieber, Larry, "Photocomposition on a COM Recorder." *The Journal of Micrographics,* May/June 1975. pp.251-254.

Teplitz, Arthur A., "Computer-Controlled Retrieval: A Primer." *The Journal of Micrographics,* September/October 1971. pp.35-40.

Chapter 6
Micrographic Standards

Standards Organizations: American National Standards Institute, National Micrographics Association, U.S. Department of Defense, U.S. National Bureau of Standards, International Standards Organization, Others • Universal Standards

Fortunately for the micrographics industry, there has been, among the people and organizations who have helped to guide the industry's growth, a constant awareness of the value of standards. This, of course, includes the principal users of the technology as well as the vendors of equipment and components. Helping to bring together these various elements have been several industrial, professional and governmental organizations whose standards efforts have tended to mesh quite smoothly over the years. The result has been a healthy industry that has seen a steady growth in the number and variety of users of its products and services, and virtually no defectors among users who have adopted micrographics for one purpose or another.

There have naturally been occasional ripples in this otherwise smooth water. But, for the most part, the constant dialog between vendors and users, through organizations like the National Micrographics Association, has effectively influenced vendors not to promote the kinds of nonstandard products that are likely to cause such ripples. Similarly, vendors have been able to influence users not to demand impractical solutions to their information-handling problems. The normal result of such dialog is compromise, and it is on compromise that practical standards are built.

Obviously, standards that are too rigid can impede utility and progress just as much as if there were no standards at all. And often the middle ground is the coexistence of dual or multiple standards on the same item. This situation exists in micrographics as in other fields. Often we will find that, on a given item, one standard that is of common benefit to multiple user communities exists side-by-side with others that meet the unique needs of specific user groups. And this is as it should be.

Following are brief profiles of the principal organizations that currently have ongoing standards programs in the micrographics field. A comprehensive index to the available published standards appears in Appendix C.

I. Standards Organizations

1. **American National Standards Institute.** The American National Standards Institute (ANSI) began life in 1918 as the American Engineering Standards Committee. It was created by the U.S. Chamber of Commerce to oversee the establishment of voluntary standards to facilitate mass production in manufacturing. It was subsequently renamed the American Standards Association (ASA), and, for a brief period in the late 1960s, was officially known as the United States of America Standards Institute (USASI). The present name was adopted in 1969, and the ANSI prefix took effect on all of the organization's existing and new standards in the fall of that year.

Of the relatively few active standards that existed when the fledgling microfilm industry began its accelerated growth in the 1950s, the majority bore the ASA label. Among the earliest were those relating to 16 and 35 mm roll film, and, to an extent, these were carry-overs of standards originally created for the motion picture industry. Today, as ANSI, this organization remains the only agency that approves national standards for the micrographics community.

ANSI's function is not to develop standards, but rather to ensure that their development by member organizations is in accordance with established procedures and that the resulting standards reflect substantial agreement among the interested and affected parties. In the micrographics field, it does this through its PH5 Committee on Micrographic Reproduction, which, since January, 1973, has had the National Micrographics Association as its Sponsor/Secretariat (replacing the American Library Association in that capacity). Among the various groups represented on PH5 are the library community, manufacturers, micropublishers, trade and professional associations, and government agencies.

2. **National Micrographics Association.** NMA came into being as the National Microfilm Association at the height of the second world war (1943) and was incorporated on a nonprofit basis shortly thereafter. (The present name became official in April, 1975.) It has been referred to variously as a trade association and a "professional forum," and it has functioned—and still does—in both capacities. In January, 1974, an organization previously known as *Users of Automatic Information Display Equipment* (UAIDE) was merged with NMA to become the latter's *Computer Image Processing* (CIP) Division.

From the outset, standardization has been one of NMA's objectives, but it was not until the 1960s that it formally inaugurated an active standards program. In 1963, before the present standards series was inaugurated, a rather flexible fiche standard was published, offering the industry a selection of sizes and formats. This approach was later abandoned in favor of the present, single-size (105 x 148 mm) standard. Among the first official publications in the current "MS" series were one on a new lettering style called *Microfont*, for the preparation of engineering drawings, and a *Glossary of Micrographics*. The latter was actually the latest in a series of updates of a document first published by NMA in 1955.

Following these two kick-off publications in the new series, the activities of various other NMA standards committees began to bear fruit, and the result has been a steadily growing list of published standards affecting all aspects of the micrographics art. NMA publishes the ANSI micrographic standards as well as its own.

3. *U.S. Department of Defense.* Together with NMA and ANSI, the Department of Defense (DOD) ranks as one of the "big three" American publishers of standards in the micrographics field. It became active in the effort at the outbreak of World War II when a crash program was launched to microfilm military engineering drawings for security purposes. Its standards relating to 35 mm film in rolls and aperture cards have served as a model for the microfilm programs of numerous civilian engineering organizations down through the years.

4. *U.S. National Bureau of Standards.* The principal function of this well-known body is to act as custodian of our national standards on weights and measures. Included in this latter category are measures of the resolving power of optical systems, and, in this connection, NBS's chief contribution to micrographic standards has been its development of the standard No. 1010 microcopy resolution test chart. (See Figure 6.1.)

    The chart was originated in 1941 under the Bureau's Standard Reference Materials program. It has been—and remains—the official standard gauge for measuring the resolution capabilities of microfilm emulsions and micrographic optical devices. The latest version, dubbed "1963-A," was introduced in December, 1967. It consists of 26 separate patterns (as compared with 21 in the previous, 1963 issue). The technical aspects of this valuable quality control tool are discussed in Chapter 7.

5. *International Standards Organization.* The International Organization for Standardization, more commonly known as *ISO*, was organized in London in 1946. It is concerned with standardization in many fields, including micrographics, and its primary functions are to coordinate the development of standards by various nations of the world, and to publish, as international standards, those on which there is substantial international agreement.

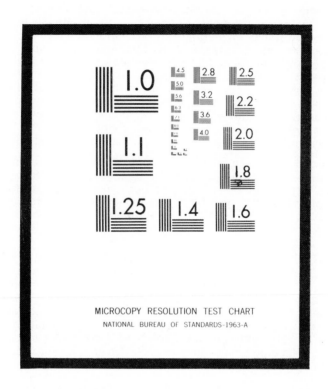

MICROCOPY RESOLUTION TEST CHART

NATIONAL BUREAU OF STANDARDS-1963-A

Figure 6.1. Despite the existence of competing designs, the NBS No. 1010 Microcopy Resolution Test Chart, here shown in its current "1963-A" configuration, has remained (since 1941) the accepted U.S. standard for resolution testing in micrographic systems.

The ISO Committee concerned with micrographics is designated TC46/SC1, "Documentary Reproduction." It consists of six working groups, their specific areas of responsibility being *microfiche, engineering drawings, newspapers, quality of microcopies, vocabulary,* and *microfilm readers and other hardware.* The United States delegation is headed by the Chairman of the ANSI PH5 Committee and includes the Chairman of the NMA Standards Board among its members.

Typical of ISO's recent micrographic standards efforts is its standardization of the *Mire* and *Micromire* legibility test charts depicted in Figure 6.2.

6. *Others.* Besides these principal standards organizations, there are many other groups that have contributed in one way or another—perhaps by participation in one or more of the above

70

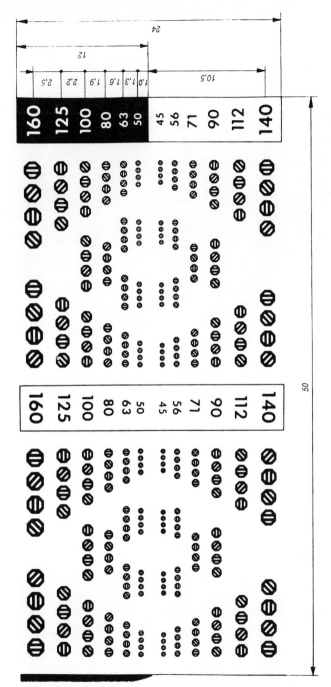

Figure 6.2, (a). The French-originated Mire *(pronounced meer) test chart is the basic microcopy legibility test standard in several countries outside the U.S. Under the designation* Mire #1, *it has been officially adopted by the ISO as an international standard. (The NBS 1010 Microcopy Resolution Test Chart is also an official international standard, designated* Mire #2 *in ISO parlance.)*

71

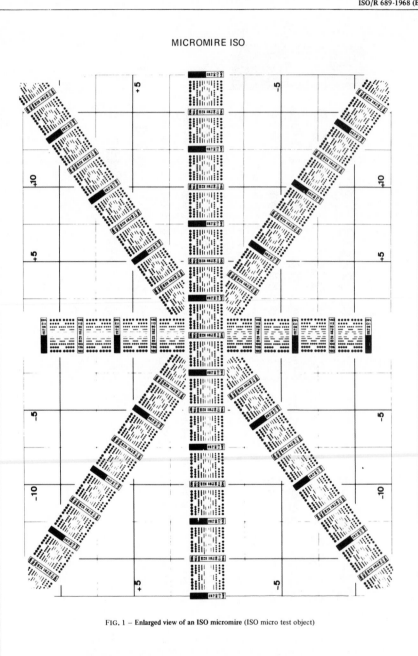

MICROMIRE ISO

FIG. 1 – Enlarged view of an ISO micromire (ISO micro test object)

Fig. 6.2, (b) The Micromire *is essentially an array of 10X-reduced Mires.*

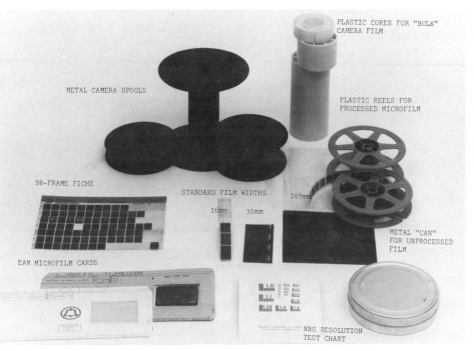

Figure 6.3. Some familiar micrographic physical items that, by their tenure and wide usage, can claim the distinction of having become universal standards.

organizations—to the total micrographic standards picture. Among them are equipment and film manufacturers, large commercial users of micrographic systems (notably in the banking and engineering communities), the Federal government (particularly the Census Bureau), and various professional user groups (the American Library Association, for example). Of the individual micrographic associations outside the U.S., those of Great Britain and France have been especially active in standards work.

II. Universal Standards

Fortunately for us here in the U.S. (or perhaps unfortunately, depending on your point of view), industry standards are usually voluntary, and the decision to abide by them is thus left to the discretion of those concerned. But, of the total, there are always bound to be some standards in any field that will be universally embraced. The micrographics field is no exception.

Besides the NBS Microcopy Resolution Test Chart, some of the more notable examples of "universal" physical standards (universal within the U.S., at least) are the 105 x 148 mm, 98-image microfiche; 16 and 35 mm film on 100 foot reels and the 35 mm E.A.M. aperture card. These and others are pictured in Figure 6.3.

There are also standards on microform production quality criteria that

73

may be considered universal. Some of these are covered in the listing of published standards that is given in Appendix C. (under 5. INSPECTION, TESTING, MEASURING). Others, not yet documented in publication, may be found in Chapter 9, in the subsection on quality control.

* * *

The next chapter will outline the various considerations that must precede the actual planning of a micrographic system.

Suggested Additional Reading

Avedon, Don M., "Standards." Series in *The Journal of Micrographics,* beginning January 1971.
Avedon, Don M., *The User's Guide to Standard Microfiche Formats.* Silver Spring, Md.: NMA, 1975. 16p.
Basic U.S. Government Micrographic Standards and Specifications. Silver Spring, Md.: NMA, 1974. 432p.
Cranwell, Gilbert S., "Problems of Establishing an International Standard for Microcopy Resolution Testing." *The Journal of Micrographics,* July/August 1974. pp.257-265.
Microfilm Norms: Recommended Standards for Libraries. Chicago, Ill.: American Library Association, 1966. 48p.
Micrographic Standards and Related Items. Resource Report #1. Silver Spring, Md.: NMA, 1974. 6p.
"New NBS Microcopy Resolution Test Charts Have Higher Frequencies." *NMA Journal,* (predecessor to the *Journal of Micrographics),* Winter 1968. pp.37-38.
The Journal of Micrographics. July/August 1971. Special issue on Standards.
White, John R., "A Case for International Graphic Standards." *The Journal of Micrographics,* Spring 1970. pp.110-122.

Chapter 7

Matching the System to the Need

*The Nature of the Input • The Desired Output •
System Capacity and Frequency of Use •
Maintenance Activity • Miscellaneous Considerations*

It can be safely surmised that virtually any conscious action an individual takes is aimed at satisfying an explicit need. If this is accepted as a maxim, it should apply as well to organizations as to individuals—though all of us can surely cite cases to the contrary.

In any event, the system planner has to proceed on two basic assumptions, namely that the new system will fulfill a definite need, and that its implementation will result in a net saving or advantage (economic or other) over alternative ways of achieving the same ends.

Obviously, the sequence of events leading to implementation of a system of any sort must begin with its having occurred to someone that there *are* alternative approaches to accomplish what has to be done. For an existing system, this implies recognition of certain deficiencies and of the probability that there is a *better* way of operating.

From that initial recognition, the logical next step, before proceeding with the actual planning of a system and selection of system components (which will be covered in Chapter 9) is to weigh all the pertinent factors involved, and thereby test the basic assumption for feasibility. In a micrographic system the essential considerations might be these:

1. nature of the input
2. desired output
3. projected system capacity
4. anticipated frequency of use
5. anticipated maintenance activity.

There are, of course, various miscellaneous considerations as well. Together with the basic ones, they constitute the "pre-planning" step in the evolution of a micrographic system, which is the subject of this chapter.

I. Nature of the Input

The very first question that has to be answered is, does the data base lend itself to microfilming? And the determining factors are, of course, its *form* and *condition*. As for what kinds of data base readily qualify for microfilming, it is quicker to list those that do not, although even that is not as simple a task as it once was.

The fact is that situations in which conversion to microform might prove impractical are becoming difficult to isolate because of the steadily expanding utility of the micrographics art. For example, it was once fairly safe to say that any documentation using colors in a way that required their retention in reproduction, as in charts, graphs and training manuals, for example, where the colors are highly significant, was *not* a candidate for micrographics. This ceased to be true a few years ago with the introduction of economically feasible color micrographic systems. Of course, in situations where there is only occasional need to preserve significant color, it would still not be feasible to adopt a total color system.

Except where original color *must* be preserved, but only for a portion of the total data base, this writer can conceive of only three kinds of situation in which the application of micrographics might prove impractical, *in some instances.* It has to be emphasized that even these situations cannot be routinely excluded from consideration. They are:

(1) any situation in which neither the quantity of documents nor *the extent to which they are irreplaceable* would justify the cost of a micrographics system even as a safeguarding expedient. For example, the routine paperwork associated with the operation of an independent hardware store in a small town (with the possible exception of microcatalogs that may be supplied by wholesalers);

(2) situations in which maps and plan drawings must, for reasons of unblemished continuity of detail, be filmed as a unified whole—*but the size of which would require too great a reduction to fit them unsectionalized, onto standard microforms with assurance of legible and undistorted reproduction.* Examples: large architectural drawings, topographical maps;

(3) situations in which the documents, in their end-use, require a degree of mobility. Example: troubleshooting procedures or schematic drawings that a craftsman must carry up a ladder with him, or that a serviceman has to use on a customer's premises. The need to use the customer's electric power to operate a reader might prove objectionable in some instances.

Items (2) and (3) require some qualification. There are many existing, and successful, micrographic systems that include "bedsheet"-size engineering and architectural plan drawings in their data base. Among the factors governing technical feasibility are the size of the smallest characters and symbols on the original drawings, the width of film used (some such systems require use of 105 mm film for dimensional stability), the degree of precision of the camera and reproduction optics, and the nature of the end-use,—whether, for example, it is sufficient to be able to view the enlarged drawing images on "scanning type" readers.

As for situations requiring document mobility, a variety of portable readers are available for such applications, including some that are battery-

Fig. 7.1. Microfiche reader specially designed for attachment to a ladder, for the use of craftsmen in telephone equipment offices, for example.

operated. Moreover, special readers have been developed for use on step-ladders by craftsmen and service technicians. (See Figure 7.1.)

In summary, then, there are virtually no paper-work situations in which the application of modern micrographic techniques can be entirely ruled out as a way of improving information storage and access.

As for the condition of the original material, that now-familiar expression, "garbage in, garbage out" was never more applicable than it is to micrographics. While a good microform camera can be a fairly forgiving device, it obviously cannot improve upon something that is only marginally legible to begin with. Also remember that, in the typical micrographic system, there may be several reproduction generations from input to the final end-use output, and there is naturally going to be a slight, but nonetheless finite, loss in quality at each step.

II. Desired Output

Among the principal questions that would have to be answered with regard to system output are:

(1) To what extent might users by willing to accept material having lower legibility than that to which they are accustomed?

(2) To what extent might they be willing to accept an image on a reader screen in lieu of hard copy?

(3) What about positive versus negative screen images? Does the data base include pictorial material that might require positive reproduction?

(4) Would something less than 1:1 reproduction be likely to cause problems?

(5) If special paper is used for hard copy reproductions, will its texture, thickness, or other physical properties be likely to cause problems?

Each of these items, plus the conducting of trials to obtain end-user reactions, will be discussed in the sub-sections that follow.

1. *Legibility*

As mentioned above, in any system involving reproduction there has to be some finite quality loss in going from one generation to another. In terms of resolution, i.e., the ability to discern separation between adjacent image elements, this loss can range from negligible, as in the contact printing of engineering drawings by the so-called "black-and-white" diazo process, to as much as *95 percent,* as in attempts to reproduce in letter-size document on a 1:1 basis via 525-line closed-circuit TV.

The standard method of measuring resolution in micrographics is by

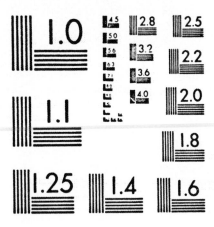

MICROCOPY RESOLUTION TEST CHART

NATIONAL BUREAU OF STANDARDS-1963-A

Fig. 7.2. National Bureau of Standards (NBS) Microcopy Resolution Test Chart.

78

Fig. 7.3. The text in this reproduced "blowback" of a microimage is quite readable despite a cumulative resolution loss in excess of 70 percent.

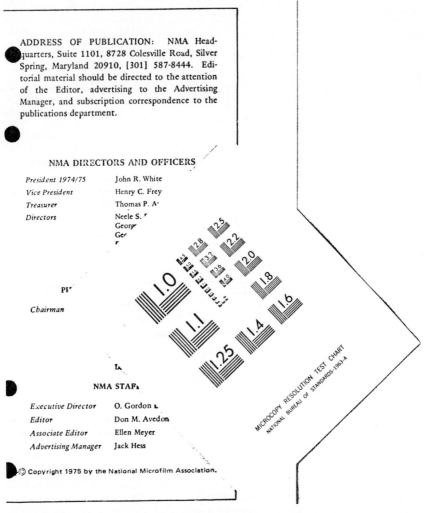

ADDRESS OF PUBLICATION: NMA Headquarters, Suite 1101, 8728 Colesville Road, Silver Spring, Maryland 20910, [301] 587-8444. Editorial material should be directed to the attention of the Editor, advertising to the Advertising Manager, and subscription correspondence to the publications department.

NMA DIRECTORS AND OFFICERS

President 1974/75	John R. White
Vice President	Henry C. Frey
Treasurer	Thomas P. A'
Directors	Neele S. ʳ
	Georʳ
	Geʳ
	r

Pl'

Chairman

Iₐ

NMA STAFₐ

Executive Director	O. Gordon ₗ
Editor	Don M. Avedon
Associate Editor	Ellen Meyer
Advertising Manager	Jack Hess

© Copyright 1975 by the National Microfilm Association.

subjectively determining the smallest pattern in which separate lines can be positively discerned in a reproduced National Bureau of Standards Microcopy Resolution Test Chart. (See Figure 7.2.) If, for example, the 2.0 pattern is the smallest one resolvable, it means that as many as 2 *spatial cycles*—black-white "line pairs"—of image detail are resolvable per millimeter of image space. If the reading has been made with the aid of a microscope on a microimage that is a 30X linear reduction of the original document, then the *actual* image resolution, relative to *real* space, is 2.0 x 30, or 60 spatial cycles per millimeter.

While this latter reading—the product of the pattern number and the

79

linear reduction—says something about the resolving capability of the film emulsion and camera optics, it is relatively insignificant from an end-use point of view. In computing a system's net resolution loss, it is sufficient to think in terms of the *number of patterns* difference between input and output resolution. Let's say, for example, that with the aid of magnification we are able to resolve the 18 pattern on the actual NBS chart, but after reducing it to film at a 24X linear reduction, and then enlarging it back 24X to a paper print, the smallest pattern resolved is the 4.0. The practical conclusion to be drawn from this is that we have sustained a net system loss of at least 16 patterns. In actual resolution, we will have gone from at least 18 cycles per millimeter at the input to only 4 cycles per millimeter at the output—*a 78 percent loss.*

This would, in fact, be a fairly normal input-output net loss for a typical micrographic system. Severe as it may seem, it results in output copy that is surprisingly legible. This fact is illustrated in figure 7.3.

Bear in mind that the print in the above example is only two generations removed from the original document. It is not uncommon for the final print or screen image to be three to four generations removed from the original. Experience has shown, however, that resolution degradation due to *contact* duplication of microimages is normally no more than one pattern per generation, and that, with quality equipment and film, the output resolution can be held to 3.5 or 4.0 cycles per mm, even after as many as four generations from the original document to final reproduction.

To an extent, the required output resolution will be linked to the particular application. In library systems, for example, or in any system where the user may be required to view a reader screen for prolonged periods, the user's *comfort* and the importance of preventing *eye fatigue* become factors, and higher resolutions may be required. A study conducted a few years ago by the Battelle Memorial Institute concluded that the *minimum* reader screen resolution for "acceptable" viewing in such systems should be 7 cycles per mm. Unfortunately, even with the present advanced state of the art, this would be a difficult objective to achieve with any degree of consistency.

Another kind of situation in which output resolution becomes a critical factor is where individual characters and symbols must be identifiable out-of-context, number lists, for example, or engineering and scientific documentation. But resolution is not the only factor in this regard. There is also the possible obliteration of image details by microscopic emulsion imperfections or specks of dust to contend with. The system's vulnerability to this potential readability impairment obviously increases in proportion to reduction ratio, and it is most likely to be encountered in comparatively dusty environments and where the microforms are subject to a relatively high degree of abuse.

2. Screen image vs hard copy

The principal determining factor here is whether (a) the document needs to be available to the user only for quick reference or (b) has to be available in a form in which it can be carried away (e.g., for use at a conference) or marked up (with changes, for example). In the former instance, a reader screen image will suffice. In the latter, hard copy is obviously required for the making of changes, and either hard copy or a duplicate microform will be required for reference at the user's work location or at a conference. Many micrographic systems are designed to provide both.

A lot depends, of course, on the nature of the data base and its function. For example, catalog pages, airline schedules, and directory pages for a telephone-directory-assistance operation will normally require only momentary reference via a reader screen, whereas engineering drawings, correspondence, and newspaper and periodical pages will often have to be available in hard copy form as well.

In terms of economics, a hard copy capability will usually mean an increase of five to ten times in the cost for each reader. The economics of a micrographic system is covered separately in the next chapter.

3. *Positive vs negative images*

The choice of tonal polarity of the reader screen image in a micrographic system, i.e., the dark-light relationship of image to background, is primarily a matter of user preference, but is likely to be influenced by the nature of the input. In a *records* system, where the normal input is alphanumeric characters and symbols of dark tone on a light background, *negative* screen images (normally, light characters and symbols on a dark background) are generally preferred for four reasons:

(1) glare is minimized;
(2) film defects (spots, scratches, etc.) and dust are less noticeable;
(3) with conventional microfilm with nonreversal* processing the normal camera output is a negative microimage, and, where diazo film is used for producing duplicates, the tonal polarity of the image does not reverse from one generation to the next;
(4) positive prints are readily producible from negative microimages.

The same applies to a system in which the input consists, wholly or in part, of line drawings and charts. Studies have shown that users adapt quite readily to the negative images on a reader screen for all these kinds of input.

Although technically the same reasoning should apply to input materials containing photographs and other *tonal graphics,* the user's reluctance to accept negative images in such cases can be appreciated. Materials in this category, such as newspaper and periodical pages, are therefore often made available to users as positive microimages. Fortunately, the con-

---

*It is important that the reader be aware of the inherent confusion in the terms *reversal, nonreversal, reversing,* and *nonreversing* with regard to film processing and the duplicating of images. The rule to remember is this: revers*al* always implies that the dark-light relationship of the images on the processed camera film is the *same* as that of the documents photographed. In other words, the result is the *reverse of that normally expected of the photographic process.* Revers*ing* has the opposite meaning—e.g., black-on-white on the original becomes white-on-black on the processed camera film. Thus revers*al* and *non*revers*ing* mean the same thing. Similarly, in contact duplication, a negative resulting from a negative or a positive resulting from a positive is revers*al* (or *non*revers*ing*), and a positive resulting from a negative or vice versa is revers*ing* (or *non*revers*al*).

gested nature of a newspaper page makes glare less a factor than it is in business correspondence and engineering drawings, for example. A possible problem in this regard, where diazo film is to be used as the distribution medium (for trade catalogs on roll film, for example), is that more involved processing may have to be used to obtain nonreversed image polarity on the camera film or, alternatively, an extra duplication generation may be required to create an intermediate master from which duplicates of the proper polarity can be produced for distribution.

Of the three basic types of film used for copying (silver, diazo and vesicular) diazo is inherently nonreversing ("direct sign") whereas silver and vesicular are normally, though not exclusively, reversing. In other words, with diazo, a negative duplicate is produced from a negative master, and a positive duplicate from a positive master; whereas, with conventional silver and vesicular copy films, a positive duplicate is normally produced from a negative master and vice versa. The exceptions are direct duplicating silver film and a recently introduced vesicular film, both of which are nonreversing. Figure 7.4 may help to clarify this matter of image polarity in the duplication process.

As mentioned in an earlier chapter, diazo images are developed by ammonia gas, and vesicular images by application of heat. Both require a detectable ultraviolet (UV) content in the exposing light source, the degree and intensity of which will determine the speed of exposure. Either type, incidentally, can be exposed to ordinary room light for short periods without damage prior to exposure and development. Both are also quite durable physically.

One further distinction between the two film types is that, under "eyeball" inspection, the tonality of the diazo images closely resembles that of the silver images from which they were produced, except that the dark portions of the diazos may have a definite color tint (blue, for example). Vesicular images, on the other hand, have a conspicuous milky appearance. In viewing or printing, however, these very obvious physical distinctions between the two types of film are generally indiscernible.

COM-generated film presents essentially the same problem as tonal graphics, but for a different reason: by nature, the original COM image, as presented to the camera lens, consists of illuminated characters and lines produced in dark surroundings, usually on the face of a CRT. Thus, with conventional nonreversal microfilm, the result is what we would normally regard as a positive master (dark characters on a light background in the processed silver microimages from the camera, i.e., a "positive-appearing image"). Where "negative appearing" screen images are preferred, the same alternatives apply as for the case where positive images are preferred in conventional source document microfilming, namely (a) reversal processing of the camera film or (b) two-step duplication, or (c) use of reversing type copy film.

4. Full-size versus reduced-size reproduction

Whether something less than a 1:1 "blowback"—i.e., an enlargement ratio that results in a print or screen image smaller than the original—will cause problems depends mainly on the size of the smallest significant

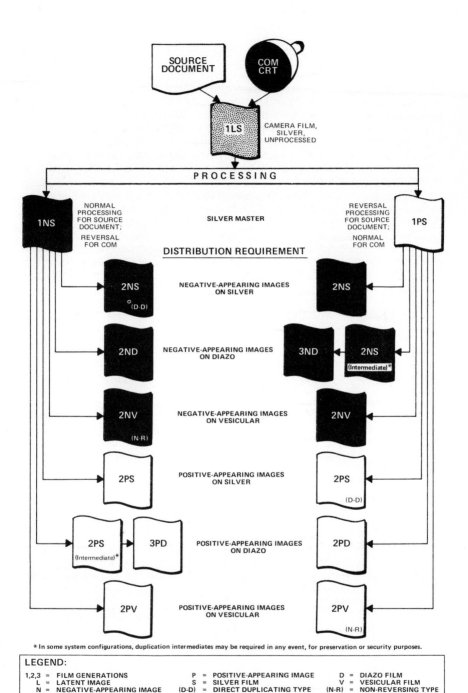

Fig. 7.4. Diagramatic illustration of image polarity in
duplicate processing.

characters and symbols likely to be encountered on the original. As a general rule, characters 1/8-inch high or larger can be reproduced half-size without any real problem to the user. This has been demonstrated by the fact that engineering drawings measuring 27" x 41" and larger are often reduced 30X onto 35 mm film and blown back 15X in the reader or on end-use hard copy. While some users do complain, the source of the complaints can usually be traced to insufficient quality control somewhere in the filming-to-reproduction chain. One very important consideration is that where characters and symbols must be individually identifiable, as in engineering drawings, for example, legibility becomes a more critical factor than it is for characters in context.

One way to increase the assurance of individual character legibility is to select, or design, a character set with that objective. NMA *Microfont* is a good example. (See Figure 7.5) It was created to minimize the confusion between various numbers, letters and symbols, and to ensure that a character's individual identity would hold up through several generations of duplication or reproduction. It accomplishes this by striking an optimum balance between stroke width and amount of white space within a character.

5. *Print paper characteristics*

In the production of enlarged prints (hard copy "blowbacks") from micro-images, there are several processes to choose from. The type of paper will usually be tied to the process, although there is a degree of flexibility. The five most commonly used processes and their characteristics are as follows:

(a) Electrolytic—a nonreversal process (positive prints from negative microimages and vice versa) that uses specially coated paper having electroconductive properties and requiring liquid chemical development. The coating is zinc-oxide, and the images tend to be low in contrast and may fade somewhat over a period of time.

(b) *Direct electrostatic*—sometimes also called *Electrofax.* * May produce either negative-appearing or positive-appearing images. Uses zinc-oxide-coated paper on which latent images are developed by application of *toner* (usually black in color) in liquid or powdered form. The toner may be either chemically fused or heat-fused to the paper. The image-to-background constrast is medium to high.

(c) *Transfer electrostatic*—often referred to as *xerography.* ** May be either reversal or nonreversal. Uses plain paper, to which the image is transferred in the form of electrostatically charged powdered toner (usually black in color), which is then heat-fused to the paper. This process is generally confined to use in stand-alone enlarger-printers, as opposed to reader-printers. The image-to-background contrast is generally quite good.

(d) *Stabilization*—a nonreversal process that uses a silver halide coated paper requiring liquid chemical development. The image-to-background contrast is medium to high, but the prints tend to discolor over a period of time.

Electrofax is a registered trademark of the RCA Corporation.
**Xerography is a generic term which actually pertains to both *direct* and *transfer* electrostatic reproduction processes.

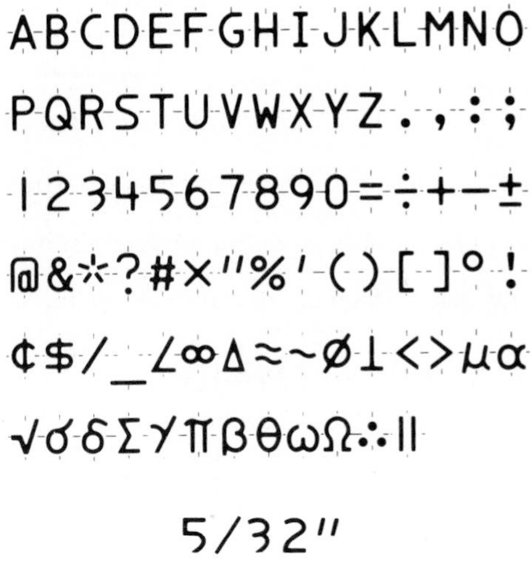

ABCDEFGHIJKLMNO

PQRSTUVWXYZ.,:;

I234567890=÷+−±

@&*?#×"%'()[ ]°!

¢$/_∠∞Δ≈~Ø⊥<>μα

√ẟẟΣγπβθωΩ∴‖

5/32"

Fig. 7.5. NMA Microfont, a special character font created specifically for use in micrographic systems.

(e)   *Dry silver*—a nonreversal process that uses a special photosensitive coating on which latent images are developed by application of heat (no chemicals required). The image-background contrast is generally quite good, but images tend to discolor over a period of time and are susceptible to destruction by exposure to excessive heat.

In all of these processes, the development of the image is automatic within the printer. The print, in all cases, emerges fully developed and ready for use.

6.   *End Use Trials*

One sure way to determine in advance the extent to which end users will accept or reject the new output format, and whether there are any hidden shortcomings inherent in it, is to run a "trial" of the proposed system prior to actual implementation. This will naturally require production of custom-made microforms and/or hard copy for the purpose, to be selectively provided to users within an actual working environment. The trial materials and associated hardware (readers, etc.) must be as nearly representative as possible of those which will ultimately be adopted.

In most cases, a brief educational program may have to precede the trial, and, in *all* cases, an objective solicitation of user reactions must follow. Reactions might be obtained by questionnaire or by personal interviews, or both. Whatever the approach, a degree of control must be exercised to ensure consistency and throughness, and the results must be objectively analyzed. It is especially important that legitimate objections or suggestions be separated out from those that result merely from resistance to change. Obviously this is not always an easy task.

Following are four basic questions that a typical end use trial should seek to answer regarding the comparative acceptance of the old and new system output formats:

(a) Is the new format as easy, less easy, or easier to use than the present one?
(b) What specific kinds of difficulties were experienced with the new format?
(c) What advantages (if any) does the new format have over the present one?
(d) In what ways might the new format be made more acceptable?

III. System Capacity and Frequency of Use

The size and anticipated rate of growth of the data base, and the frequency at which a file must be accessed, are primarily system design considerations, to be dealt with in the next stage of development. However, to the extent that these factors influence the decision to go the micrographics route in the first place, and to effectively match the system to the need, these are some of the questions that may need answering:

(1) Is the data base large enough or growing fast enough to warrant its conversion to microform?
(2) How much work will the initial conversion involve, and what provisions must be made for a continuing program of paper-to-film conversion?
(3) How big an investment will be required in new filing and retrieval facilities, and how much flexibility should be allowed for future growth?
(4) Will the volume of usage be sufficient to justify consideration of an automated retrieval capability?
(5) Assuming a high volume situation and automated retrieval, will the system be able to respond to multiple inquiries simultaneously?

As a general rule, the larger the quantity of documents involved, the better the case for micrographics. Proceeding from that basic premise, the remaining questions become particularly important, and these will be explored in greater depth in subsequent chapters. For the moment, a couple of points should be kept in mind relative to questions (3) through (5). One is the importance of a realistic estimate of the frequency with which the microform file is likely to be accessed, particularly during peak activity periods. This will determine not only the amounts of viewing, duplicating and reproduction equipment required, but also whether it might be expedient, in some situations, to maintain duplicate master files, or to automate the file in some degree. The second point is that, where a *queuing* problem may arise occasionally in a strictly manual system, it can generally be solved by adding extra clerks or by re-distributing the file's work force as required, whereas an automated retrieval system might have to be somewhat over-engineered to cope with a similar situation when it occurs.

These points are primarily economic matters, and will be considered in that context in the next chapter. They will also be covered in Chapter 9 from the standpoint of system design.

IV. Maintenance Activity

The word *maintenance,* as used here, refers to the up-keep of the file. That includes addition of completely new material, replacement of existing material with reissues, and weeding or purging of the file to eliminate superseded or otherwise invalid material.

One point to keep in mind regarding maintenance of *any* micrographic system is that each new and changed original document requires production of a new microimage. The amount of work and cost that this entails will vary with the type of microform. With roll film or jackets, for example, it is possible (though perhaps not practical) to add individual microimages without having to re-film whole groups of associated documents, as is normally the case with multi-image *unit* microforms like microfiche. In a roll film system, added images might have to be spliced to the end of an existing roll. An exception to this rule for the multi-image unit media is a revolutionary imaging technology recently introduced which permits new images to be added to existing blank frames on the already-processed master.

One advantage of a *unitized* microform system (notably aperture cards and fiche), as compared with its paper counterpart, is that file maintenance is somewhat simplified by the sheer uniformity and reduced bulk of the medium. The task can, in fact, be automated to some extent. As pointed out in Chapter 4, some automated unitized systems permit completely random filing of the unit microforms, a feature that has obvious advantages in the policing and updating of a busy file.

To sum up, high activity in file maintenance should be no deterrent to the microfilming of an existing paper file. It may, however, influence the choice of microform and the general type of system adopted.

V. Miscellaneous Considerations

Among other considerations influencing the decision to adopt a micrographic system are (1) the use of color in the data base, (2) the possible need to remotely access the file, (3) the degree of file security required, and (4) the legal aspects of micrographics. Let's briefly examine each of these:

1. Use of color

As previously mentioned, it is no longer true that microfilming is precluded where color is an essential element of the data base. However, while color microfilm has become a commercial reality and has been put to active use in some quarters, particularly in merchandising applications, there are still a couple of formidable obstacles to its feasibility for many prospective applications. One is cost, as the film alone can cost up to five times as much as black-and-white, and the other is the need for highly specialized duplication and reproduction equipment.

Generally speaking, color output from a micrographic system is likely to prove feasible in comparatively few special applications. Outside of merchandising programs in which color microforms (usually fiche) are distributed in connection with product promotion, other possibilities are their use in the micropublishing of periodicals in which the use of color is considered significant; in systems using micrographics to expedite retrieval of maps and charts; and as a means of inexpensively distributing sets of color "slides", for use in training programs, for example.

2. Remote access

The need to remotely access a file will generally be facilitated by the adoption of micrographics. Theoretically, the cost of a remote accessing capability alone (e.g., closed-circuit TV) should be essentially the same whether the file is microform or hard copy. The basic technical difference, as explained in Chapter 5, will be in the optics of the transmitting device—TV camera or fax scanner.

The advantages the micrographic system has over hard copy for remote accessing are (1) uniformity of input, and (2) the facilitation of automated remote retrieval of specific documents. The first of these advantages needs some qualification: in a system in which more than one reduction ratio is used, such as an engineering drawing system, the fact that the microform is of uniform size and shape regardless of the reduction ratio of the images it contains means that, in effect, we are trading off output uniformity for input uniformity. Looking at it in terms of number of scan lines per character height, with ten the generally recommended minimum for assured legibility of individual characters, and recognizing that the number of scan lines per given linear dimension at the input is generally fixed, each character in a 30X-reduced image will be dissected by about half the number of scan lines as a 16X-reduced character. The output legibility will vary accordingly.

One solution is the use of closed-circuit TV with a zoom capability. But, in any event, the matter of trade-offs, between cost, resolution, and speed, is an important consideration in the planning of any remote access micrographic system.

3. Security

Like remote access, security is generally enhanced with a micrographic system, for a couple of reasons. One is that hard copy is readily reproducible on conventional office copiers, whereas reproduction of microimages requires equipment that is not, as yet, quite so ubiquitous. The other is that, in a micrographic system, the microform master need never leave the file in tangible form. An image on a reader screen will suffice in many cases, and a fully automated retrieval capability provides the added assurance that the microform master is normally secure from human handling.

In fact, the combination of remote accessing and the inherent security aspects of micrographics can add up to a system that offers maximum security. The remotely accessed master file can, for example, be placed within a locked vault, and authorized retrieval at the remote stations can be easily controlled by assignment of special accessing codes.

4. Legal aspects

Although the general situation has eased considerably in recent years, there are still some legal obstacles to microfilming that prospective users should be aware of. From the standpoint of admissibility as evidence in courts of law, microfilm has been accepted in lieu of original documents in *all* Federal courts and in most state and local courts in this country since 1951. However, to ensure admissibility, the microfilmer must abide by certain procedural requirements affecting film quality and content. These are:

(a) the documents must be recorded in their entirety with no excerpting or cropping;

(b) the images must be judged legible when optically enlarged for viewing;

(c) it must be ascertainable that the documents have been accurately recorded and that the act of converting them to microfilm falls within the scope of normal business routine.

Requirement (c) is generally satisfied by microfilming, along with the documents, a form or forms containing appropriate certifications that the basic requirements have been met. Examples are shown in Figure 7.6.

In addition to these basic requirements, some governmental agencies may have special rules regarding retention of original documents or duplicate microfilm files. The prospective micrographics user is urged to investigate such matters within the particular sphere of his operations. In the case of an operation that crosses national boundaries, it is also important to familiarize one's self with the laws regarding microfilm in each of the affected countries.

Another legal aspect of micrographics, and one that is somewhat less settled than the question of admissibility of evidence, is its involvement with copyright law. Basically, the best advice in this regard is simply not to microfilm anything copyrighted without having first secured the permission of the copyright holder. This also applies to the duplicating or printing of microform masters obtained from an outside source.

Fig. 7.6. Typical forms of the sort required for inclusion on each unit microform to satisfy legal obligations.

CERTIFICATE OF AUTHENTICITY

THIS IS TO CERTIFY that the microphotographs appearing on this Film-File starting with

_____ and ending with

_____ are accurate and

complete reproductions of the records of (Company and Dept.) _____

_____ as delivered in the regular course of business for photographing.

Date produced _____   _____
              (Month)   (Day)   Camera Operator

Place _____
      (City)   (State)

89

DECLARATION OF INTENT AND PURPOSE

I, _____ , employed by _____ ,

do hereby declare that the records microfilmed herein are actual records of the _____

_____ created during its normal course of business and that:

It is the express intent and purpose of this organization to destroy or otherwise dispose of the original

records microphotographed herein, and that:

The destruction or disposition of the records microphotographed on this reel is only to be accomplished

after inspection of the microfilm to assure completeness of coverage, and that:

It is the policy of this organization to microfilm and dispose of original records in accordance with customer

authorization or as part of the planned organizational operating procedure.

Date _____ 19___ _____
     (Month)   (Day)   Signature

Place _____ _____
     (City)   (State)   Title

_____
                                     Company

Copyright holders are naturally reluctant to grant permission to microfilm their works because of the relative ease with which the master microform can be reproduced. This is especially true of fiche, which permit 98 or more pages to be duplicated at once.

At present, the relationship of copyright law to photocopying activity is somewhat nebulous. A lot hinges on the final outcome of the landmark *Williams & Wilkins* case, involving photocopying of medical periodicals in U.S. Government libraries in connection with interlibrary loans. Initially, the *Williams & Wilkins Company,* publisher of the specific periodicals in question, sued the government and won a decision granting recovery of "reasonable and entire compensation" for such infringement. Subsequently, that decision was overturned on appeal, and the reversal was, in effect, upheld on February 25, 1975 when the U.S. Supreme Court's review of the case resulted in a tie vote. At the time of writing, the only direct legal avenue remaining open to the plaintiff is a petition for a rehearing. However, the prevailing speculation is that the photocopying question that is at the heart of the Williams and Wilkins case will ultimately be settled only by an Act of Congress. Whatever the final outcome, it is bound to have an impact on certain aspects of microreproduction. The matter bears watching.

* * *

Besides matching the system to the need, it is well to have some idea of what it is going to cost. The next chapter explores the basic economic considerations in the planning of a micrographic system.

Suggested Additional Reading

Admissibility in Evidence of Microfilm Records. Silver Spring, Md.: NMA, 1971. 116p.
Bock, D. Joleen, "Microform Usage in 2-Year Colleges." *The Journal of Micrographics,* May/June 1974. pp.231-233.
Blunt, Charles R., "Solving Information Problems: Is Microfilm the Answer?" *NMA Proceedings, 1973.* Silver Spring, Md.: NMA. pp.II-108—II-156.
Brown, Connis O., Jr., "The Case Against 'Fore and Aft' Certification." *The Journal of Micrographics,* March/April 1974. pp.149-153.
Bujkovsky, Gustav J., "Microfilming of Large Size Drawings." *The Journal of Micrographics,* October/November 1970. pp.13-16.
Christ, C.W., Jr., "Microfiche: A Study of User Attitudes and Reading Habits." *Journal of the American Society of Information Science,* January/February 1972. pp.30-35.
Edwards, Mary Jane, "Microforms: A View From the State Library of Pennsylvania." *The Journal of Micrographics,* May/June 1975. pp.245-250.
Fair, Judy, "The Microtext Reading Room." *Microform Review.* Series beginning in July 1972.
Frey, Henry C., "Microfilm User Equipment Demands." *The Journal of Micrographics,* May/June 1972. pp.233-235.
Goodchild, Lester C., "Keeping the Court Record Straight." *Government Data Systems,* May/June 1974. pp.18-19, 34.
Gordon, Ronald F., "Microform Programs and Operations at DDC." *The Journal of Micrographics,* May/June 1972. pp.229-231.
Gray, Edward, "The Elusive Pursuit of Copyright in Micropublishing." *The Journal of Micrographics,* September/October 1974. pp.47-48.
Guide to Record Retention Requirements. Washington, D.C.: U.S. Government Printing Office, 1972. 91p.
Harmon, George H., "Is Microfilm Ready for Classroom Use?" *The Journal of Micrographics,* May/June 1972. pp.257-260.
Harrison, Tom L., "Evaluating Microfilm Applications." *The Journal of Micrographics,* July/August 1972. pp.301-309.

Hawken, W.R., *Copying Methods Manual.* Chicago, Ill.: American Library Association, 1966. 375p.
Henry, Nicholas L., "Copyright, Public Policy, and Information Technology." *Science,* February, 1974. pp.384-391.
Kish, Joseph L., Jr., "The Legality of Microfilm Records." *Business Graphics,* August 1974. p.30.
Kolb, John, "Microfilm in Government Today." *Government Data Systems,* January/February 1974. pp.16-17, 27.
Lee, Thomas G., *Microform Systems: A Handbook for Educators.* Ann Arbor, Mich.: Michigan Audio-Visual Association, 1970. 65p.
Nadel, Eli, "Microfilm—A Systems View." *The Journal of Micrographics,* Summer 1970. pp.195-202.
Nelson, Carl E., *Microfilm Technology: Engineering and Related Fields.* New York, N.Y.: McGraw-Hill, 1965. 397p.
Nelson, Carl E., *Modern Drafting Techniques for Quality Microreproduction.* Silver Spring, Md.: NMA, 1971. 38p.
Orne, Jerrold, "Microforms and the Research Library." *NMA Proceedings, 1970.* Silver Spring, Md.: NMA. pp.54-61.
Renner, Will F., "Color Microfiche as a Self-Instructional Medium." *NMA Proceedings, 1974.* Silver Spring, Md.: NMA. pp.II-295—II-299.
Rochlin, Phillip, "Micro Media in the Library: A Once Over Lightly." *The Journal of Micrographics,* January/February 1973. pp.99-104.
Santen, Vernon B., "Certification." *The Journal of Micrographics,* January/February 1975. p.143.
Smith, Chandler, "Color Microfiche for Teaching Anatomic Pathology." *The Journal of Micrographics,* January 1971. pp.83-86.
Spaulding, Carl M, "New Uses of Microforms in the Library." *NMA Proceedings, 1973.* Silver Spring, Md.: NMA. pp.II-293—II-298.
Stevens, Stanley D., "Microfilming Maps in Color." *NMA Proceedings, 1971.* Silver Spring, Md.: NMA. pp.II-48—II-50.
Teplitz, Arthur A., "Microfilm Libraries—Service Levels and Impact of Copyright on These Levels." *The Journal of Micrographics,* November/December 1972. pp.67-70.
The Journal of Micrographics, July/August 1973. Three articles dealing with the relationship of copyright law to micropublication:
   1) Lee, Edward M., Jr., "Two Views on Copyright Laws and Their Effect on the Information Industry." p.237.
   2) Reville, Charles O., "The Williams and Wilkins Company vs. the United States: Another Charge of the Light Brigade." pp.238-239.
   3) Freedman, Samuel B., "Unofficial Copyright As It Applies to Micropublications." pp.240-242.
Thomas, Alfred J., "Color Slides on Microfiche Saves Space, Time, Money." *The Journal of Micrographics,* May/June 1974. pp.221-222.
Wilber, Alan W., "Microfiche Systems for the Small User." *The Journal of Micrographics,* January/February 1972. pp.131-136.
Wiest, D.G., "Film: The Durable Medium." *Special Libraries,* November 1971. pp.475-480.

Chapter 8

Economics

Elements of an Economic Analysis • Filming and Processing • Filing and Retrieval Facilities • Duplicating and Distribution • Display and Reproduction Equipment • Miscellaneous Items

The first thing that should occur to anyone considering adoption of a micrographic system is that the anticipated economies are going to be offset somewhat by the need for special equipment and processes that are not required in a paper system. Probably the most obvious of these are the readers or reader-printers (or both), without which anything but a strictly archival or disaster file would be useless.

But readers and reader-printers are just one offsetting economic element. Another may be the need to convert an existing paper file to microform, both initially and on a continuing basis as new paper is generated. Other elements are the different storage facilities that will be required, and the peripheral equipment and materials such as duplicators, inspection apparatus, and expendable film, print paper and chemicals. In a complete "do-it-yourself" operation involving source documents, there will be the additional need for at least one microfilming camera and a film processor, along with perhaps some EDP equipment, and the skilled or semiskilled labor that will be required to operate all of these relatively sophisticated devices.

As discouraging as all this may sound, the fact is that there are few instances in which the necessary investment cannot be justified and in which a net saving, whether implicit or explicit, will not result from the adoption of micrographics. However, this statement involves three fundamental assumptions: (1) that there was fairly obvious margin for improvement in the previous mode of operation; (2) that the promised net saving will not necessarily be realized immediately; and (3) that the system has been properly planned and implemented with respect to the particular end requirements. All of these represent conditions that are relatively easy to meet in practically any situation.

By way of example, let's take a moment to analyze the economics of a couple of actual systems in which significant net savings are clearly identifiable.

First, a large system: the Federal Government's so-called "MINICATS" program for miniaturization of defense supply catalogs of the vast array of items used or purchased by the U.S. Department of Defense. Formerly published in paper form, the catalogs are currently being converted to COM-generated 48X microfiche, and will eventually be available exclusively in that form. The difference in production cost between the old and new systems is, in itself, substantial: 16 cents per thousand pages on fiche, compared with upwards of two dollars per thousand pages of hard copy.

At the current production volume of approximately *two billion* distributed pages a year, the annual saving in production cost alone is in the neighborhood of four million dollars, which is enough to directly finance about half the 35,000 readers and 1,000 reader-printers that have been ordered for implementation of the program. In addition, there are substantial savings to be realized in distribution, maintenance, and storage. Once the program is fully underway and start-up costs have been recovered, continuous savings of several million dollars a year are virtually guaranteed.

On a smaller scale, a bank in Virginia is realizing savings of more than $7,500 a year as a result of having converted its mortgage records from paper to jacketed microfilm. More than a million separate documents are involved, and the total file is not only highly active, but had occupied more than 900 square feet of valuable space when it was in paper form.

In addition to an equipment investment of about $18,000, which includes 30 readers and all necessary production and filing equipment, there is an annual cost of slightly more than $2,000 for supplies and for maintenance contracts on the equipment. Amortizing the equipment investment over a period of 10 years* brings the total annual cost of the new system to approximately $4,000. This cost is more than offset, however, by an annual saving of $7,000 on a net reduction of staff by one person and an estimated annual saving of $4,500 for reclaimed floor space. Hence, the net $7,500-a-year saving.

To round out the picture, here are just two other examples of specific areas in which real cost savings have accrued to business concerns from the application of micrographics:

1) A single branch office of a large insurance company realized a 60 percent labor saving through elimination of an entire night shift, the sole function of which had been to refile the paper documents that had been pulled for reference in the course of the preceding business day;

2) The substitution of COM devices for line printers in a New York banking chain resulted in an annual saving of $75,000 in paper costs alone.

Like snowflakes, there are probably no two micrographic system case histories in which the cost-saving objectives and experiences are exactly alike. And there are few cases on record in which a micrographic system, once implemented, failed to yield a net economic gain.

---

*As will be seen in the discussion of depreciation, which follows, the choice of 10 years as the amortization period for micrographic equipment may be debatable in some quarters.

I. Elements of an Economic Analysis

It is not the purpose of this chapter to serve as a tutorial on how to conduct an economic analysis. It will not, for example, get into the intricacies of *depreciation accounting,* nor the relationship of *cash flow* to a system's economic feasibility. However, a few words on some of the basic considerations are certainly in order.

First, one of the essential elements in analyzing the economics of any system involving the purchase of durable equipment is *depreciation.* There are several ways of figuring it, but two of them tend to predominate in general accounting practice. One is the *cash flow* method, which is influenced by income tax laws and which treats annual cost in nonlinear fashion, and the other is the *straight line* approach, which some accountants speak of as being applied for "book purposes". Both function to spread the expenditure for purchase of equipment over a period of time representing the anticipated useful life of the equipment. This time span is known variously as the *amortization, payout,* or *write-off* period, and it tends to be somewhat shorter and less linear for the cash flow method than for the straight-line.

For a general assessment of system feasibility, the less involved straight-line approach will usually suffice. But, because it is generally safer to err on the high side in estimating the annual cost of a system, the shorter write-off periods reflected in government guidelines (see below) may be preferred.

Apart from tax laws, there are several other factors that influence the depreciation of equipment, among them its inherent durability, the intensity with which it is used, and the impact of obsolescence due to technological advances that occur within its life span. Whatever the criteria, different amortization periods tend to apply for different categories of durable goods and equipment. A manufacturing concern, for example, may write-off jigs and fixtures in 2 years, and machine tools in 20. Similarly, typewriters are sometimes amortized in a much shorter time than reproduction equipment. Following are some current government guidelines for *Asset Depreciation Ranges* on items of interest to the micrographic systems planner:

1. Office appliances, reproduction equipment*: 5 years
2. Computer peripherals: 5 years
3. Communications equipment: 5 to 8 years
4. Office furniture, filing hardware: 8 years
5. Computer mainframes: 5 to 10 years

Technically, the anticipated *salvage value* of the equipment at the end of its useful life should be deducted from the actual purchase price (including sales tax and other "extras"), and this reduced figure should be the one on which the write-off is based. Granted, it may be difficult to determine what the salvage value of a microform reader will be 5 years from now, but one cost analyst's guess in probably as good as another's.

---

*For economic analysis purposes, this category includes most of the "active" micrographic equipment (cameras, processors, readers, etc.)

Another important factor in the economics of a micrographic system is *maintenance cost.* Micrographic equipment contains mechanisms that are subject to wear and misadjustment and components that are breakable or that have limited life. Hence there will be maintenance costs associated with its use. As a general rule, the anticipated annual maintenance cost may be figured as 10 percent of the purchase price of the equipment. Some economists, however, will question this figure on the basis of its failure to reflect the shifting balance between production and maintenance labor costs.

When equipment is rented rather than purchased, the annual cost will usually add up to between 1/2 and 1/3 of the purchase price. This will, of course, vary with the vendor's schedule for recovering development costs of a new product, his competitive posture, and so forth. In addition, there may be a one-time installation charge. Maintenance will normally be included in the rental change.

The remaining primary considerations are *floorspace* and, of course, *labor.* The first of these will be discussed in general terms in the section on *Filing and Retrieval Facilities* later in the chapter, and typical space requirements will be covered in the discussions of equipment costs. A word of clarification on the hardware space requirements shown in the various tables throughout the remainder of this chapter: they pertain to the *equipment alone* and do not include operating space or the space for tables and stands on which some of the equipment may have to be placed. In planning the physical layout of the micrographic system, appropriate allowances must be made for these additional space requirements, where applicable. (See Chapter 9.)

About all that need be said further about floor-space at this point is that, as a general guideline, annual costs can range roughly from $10 per square foot in rural areas to $100 per square foot in metropolitan areas. These figures are usually "loaded" with virtually every conceivable cost associated with the ownership or use of a building—taxes, depreciation, lighting, heating, grounds maintenance, etc. There will be variations, however, in how the precise figure is arrived at and how it is applied. Some companies, for example, include in their loaded salary figures the cost of the floor-space occupied by the individual. This must be taken into account where both floor-space and labor are included as cost elements in an economic study.

As for labor, *per se,* an accurate appraisal of the savings that can be expected through the application of micrographics will require a time and motion study of the present operation. The study results, along with what is known of the capabilities of the types of micrographic equipment being considered, should yield a fair picture of what can be expected in the way of labor savings. The term *labor savings,* as applied in this chapter, incidentally, will be assumed to embrace *productivity* as one of its elements. Granted, it is a difficult element to measure quantitatively, but an important one nonetheless.

Among the specific questions that will need to be answered concerning the labor factor are these:

96

1. What are the present steps required to enter a new document into the file, and how does this compare, in terms of time consumed, with the micrographics approach, where original paper (or perhaps digital data) must be converted to film?
2. What is the present turnaround time for manually retrieving a specific document, and how does it compare with what can reasonably be expected if the same document were more conveniently filed in microform? For example, how much less walking time would be involved on the part of a file clerk? Turnaround time on requests can affect user productivity as well as clerical labor requirements.
3. What is the present time required for *re*filing, and how does it compare with what could reasonably be expected if the same document were more conveniently filed in microform?
4. To what extent are retrieval and refiling delays incurred by previous *mis*filing of documents under the present system?
5. To what extent is the present file accessed simultaneously by more than one person, and to what extent does this result in retrieval and refiling delays? This question relates to the fact that, in microform, not only is the file likely to be confined to a much smaller physical area, but multiple document pages may be contained on the same unit microform. The answer may indicate which microform it would be best to use, and whether duplicate master microform files will be required.
6. What are the possibilities that the micrographic approach would permit more convenient locating of the file, and what might this mean in terms of "travel" time, within or between premises, on the part of those who must regularly access the file?
7. In what ways will the adoption of micrographics be likely to impact on the training of personnel and on the skills and responsibilities required of them?

One final point on economic analysis: though it is customary to reduce all system expenditures to the common denominator of annual costs that are repeated (more or less) over the course of several years, it is well to distinguish separately those that will remain in force for the life of the system. Basically, they are:

1. File maintenance costs (filming, refilming, film processing, purchase of film and chemicals, updating and purging the file)*
2. space costs
3. labor associated with the provision of service to file users
4. expendable materials associated with file service (print paper, duplicate film, chemicals, etc.)
5. equipment rentals
6. electronic transmission (for remote file accessing)

These and other cost elements will be outlined and discussed in the remainder of this chapter.

II. Filming and Processing

Having briefly analyzed some actual examples of the economic benefits of micrographics in an active paper records environment, let's now look at

---

*Including related labor costs.

micrographic systems in general, examining the basic cost elements in somewhat greater depth. Where examples of specific costs are given in this section, and in those that follow, bear in mind that they are as at the time of writing, in mid-1975.

One of the first questions that has to be answered in assessing the economics of the projected system is where the filming and processing will be done, and by whom. In this context, *filming* applies to both source document filming with a microfilm camera and the conversion of digital data to microimages via COM.

First, there are two phases to consider: (1) the initial conversion of the existing file to microform, and (2) the continuing program of filming new material entering the file. In either phase, the filming or processing—or both—can be done either in-house or outside, and it still remains to be decided who will do what. The various possibilities are shown in Table A.

TABLE A

Various divisions of responsibility for filming and processing in the implementation of a micrographic system.

	INITIAL CONVERSION		CONTINUING PROGRAM	
	FILMING	PROCESSING	FILMING	PROCESSING
1.	in-house by user	in-house by user	in-house by user	in-house by user
2.	in-house by user	outside by vendor	in-house by user	in-house by user
3.	in-house by user	outside by vendor	in-house by user	outside by vendor
4.	in-house by vendor	outside by vendor	in-house by user	in-house by user
5.	in-house by vendor	outside by vendor	in-house by user	outside by vendor
6.	in-house by vendor	outside by vendor	outside by vendor	outside by vendor
7.	outside by vendor	outside by vendor	in-house by user	in-house by user
8.	outside by vendor	outside by vendor	in-house by user	outside by vendor
9.	outside by vendor	outside by vendor	outside by vendor	outside by vendor

In this table, *in-house by user* implies purchase or rental of the necessary equipment by the user for regular, on-premises use. *In-house by vendor* refers to the temporary installation by the vendor of filming facilities on the user's premises for the duration of the initial conversion, and *outside by vendor* refers to filming and/or processing performed by an outside service bureau on its own premises.

98

Configuration number 1 would apply where the decision has been made to purchase the filming and processing equipment at the outset, or perhaps to rent it with an option to purchase, and where the user wishes, therefore, to get maximum use from it and can spare the necessary extra labor for its operation during the initial conversion phase. The decision to purchase the equipment at the outset might be in anticipation of a price rise, or perhaps because a study has shown that the initial conversion can be accomplished at less cost, though probably more slowly, that way. Whatever the reasoning involved, this is obviously one of the first decisions that have to be made in assessing the total system cost.

Configurations 2 and 3 differ only in the extent to which the user intends to have the film processing done outside. If the initial conversion is to be a crash program involving a large number of documents, and even though processing may be done in-house for the continuing program, the initial phase will probably require a much larger capacity facility than will be needed later. It therefore makes sense, under the circumstances, to use an outside processing service at least initially.

Configurations 4, 5 and 6 assume a situation in which, for one reason or another, it would be inadvisable to permit any part of the data base to leave the premises. Thus the service bureau must install cameras on the customer's premises for the duration of the initial file conversion. This is a fairly common practice where the data base is large or otherwise difficult and costly to move, or where there is an element of security involved.

In the last three configurations, the data base is physically removed from the premises and delivered to a service bureau for conversion to microform. In configuration 9, the service bureau continues to perform both filming and processing after the initial conversion is complete and the program has entered its continuing phase.

Besides the economics, which will be analyzed later in this chapter, other factors that may influence the decision to use a service bureau instead of establishing one's own in-house operation are: (1) the assurance the customer has that the work is being done by skilled professionals, and (2) the comforting knowledge that chronic problems such as equipment failure and obsolescence and employee turnover remain those of the vendor, although, obviously, the cost of these problems is ultimately going to be reflected in the vendor's charges for the service he provides.

For the user who wants to "go it alone", Table B shows some typical equipment costs and space requirements for in-house filming and processing facilities at the time of writing. The range of purchase prices for a given item is largely a function of the variety of capabilities. All of the items may, of course, be rented rather than purchased, and as for the COM device, an existing one may be time-shared, in which case normal programming and computer time costs will apply.

It has been estimated, incidentally, that the crossover point at which an in-house COM operation begins to prove-in economically over the use of a service bureau is likely to occur at a production volume of somewhere under a million pages (frames) a month, and that the system can be expected to cost better than $10,000 a month to maintain. A system to produce the same volume of paper output might cost twice as much.

Generalized space requirements, capabilities, and costs for in-house microfilming and film processing devices

DEVICE	SELECTABLE CAPABILITIES	SIZE		APPROXIMATE PRICE RANGE ($)
		SQ. FT.	HEIGHT (IN.)	
ROTARY (FLOW) CAMERA	• multiple reductions • automatic exposure control • interchangeable film units • automatic warnings (end of film, etc.) • variable film lengths • variable frame sizes • selectable formats (simplex, duo, etc.) • automatic "blip" marking • auto-feed • exposure counter • strip film output • throughputs from 60 to over 600 pages per minute	1-8	6-60	1600 - 10,000 (avg. : 5000)
STRAIGHT PLANETARY CAMERA	Most of the above, plus... • projected frame field indicator • backlighting • vacuum platen • automatic focus • variable film advance • 100 to 200-ft. film capacity	2-130	12-132	830 - 15,650 (avg. : 5000)
STEP & REPEAT PLANET. CAMERA (105 mm)	Generally the same as for straight planetary, plus ... • conformance to various fiche formats • automatic column and row advance • special holder for book filming • automatic page-turner • semi-automated page feed	7-20	22-74	7950 - 63,600 (avg. : 25,000)
CAMERA-PROCESSOR	Generally the same as for straight planetary or rotary, plus ... • may be capable of handling two or more different microforms • units available for roll film, cut fiche, or aperture cards.	5-25	16-77	2950 - 12,970 (avg. : 9000)
COM DEVICE	• selectable code formats (ASCII, EBCDIC, etc.) • CRT monitor • integral controller • interchangeable film units • up to 1000 ft. capacity • retrieval coding • graphics capability • integral tape drive • forms overlay capability • card reader • error correction • variable effective reductions • selectable fonts & sizes • 7 or 9-track tape • integral fiche cutter • integral film processor • throughputs from average 5 to average 600 pages a minute	6-28	42-72	32,400 - 385,000 (or 1-7.5K/month) (avg. : 100,000, or 3.5K/month)
FILM PROCESSOR, COMPACT, OFFICE TYPE	• acceptance of various film sizes • self-threading capability • leaderless feed • magazine loading • automatic control of solution temperatures • automatic warnings (dryer failure, low solution levels, etc.)• reversal processing • automatic agitation of solutions • dyeback scrubbing • film capacity up to 1000 ft. • plumbingless installation • automatic solution replenishment • throughputs from 60 to 800 ft. per hour	1-14	10-30	1680 - 5750 (avg. : 4000)
FILM PROCESSOR, LARGE, PRODUCTION TYPE	Generally the same as for office type, but ... • film capacity up to 3000 ft. or more • throughputs up to 12,000 ft. per hour	3-80	38-120	4195 - 20,000 (avg. : 10,500)

Besides equipment costs, and depending on the type of system, there will be the following representative costs for expendables:

FILM, SILVER-HALIDE PER 100 FT. ROLL-
  16 mm: $ 4.00 to $ 5.00
  35mm: $ 6.00 to $ 8.50
  105mm: $20.00 to $25.00

APERTURE CARDS (NO FILM): APPROX. $15 PER THOUSAND
  (for a purchase of approximately 100,000 cards)

PROCESSING CHEMICALS, PER 100 FT. OF FILM-

   16mm: approx. $ 0.15
   35mm: approx. $ 0.30
  105mm: approx. $ 0.90

These chemical costs assume a relatively efficient processing operation—one in which the chemicals are used fairly constantly before they have to be dumped and renewed. Apart from a given amount of film, there is also a time element associated with each new chemical "loading." Five days is the usual limit, regardless of how little film may have been processed in that time.

One "fringe" cost not to be overlooked in connection with in-house processing is the one-time cost for provision of special plumbing, where required. This will usually involve not only a precision mixing valve to ensure proper water temperatures, but the required waste facilities as well. Depending on circumstances (facilities already available, local ordinances, etc.), the cost could range anywhere from a couple of hundred dollars to a few thousand.

Where the alternative of contracting the work out to a service bureau is contemplated, a detailed specification of end requirements, including a description of the data base, will be required as the basis for a *Request For Quotation* (RFQ) to be submitted to two or more prospective vendors. In a digital data situation involving conversion from impact printing to COM, the customer has to realize that magnetic tape formatted for impact printing may not always be directly applicable as the input to a COM device. Where this is the case, the usual solution is to provide special software that will permit the production of COM-compatible tapes for use by the service bureau. This accommodation can be made either by the customer, in cooperation with his own data processing people, or by the service bureau itself.

In any dealings with a service bureau, the drafting of a specification will normally have been preceded by discussions between the customer and prospective vendors about the latter's capabilities and limitations, and possibly the customer's need to temper his end requirements to keep them within the realm of practicality. This is perhaps best achieved by the customer's hosting a "bidder's meeting," with representatives of at least two competing service bureaus present. A good specification will reflect what has been learned from such preliminary discussions. Following are sample summaries of the basic items to be specified for both the source document and COM systems. The specific data (amounts, etc.) are hypothetical.

1.   *Source Document*

   (a) Data base to be filmed will consist of some 500,000 loose, letter-size paper pages of varying content and condition.
   (b) Pages shall be reduced 24X onto 16mm roll film, "comic" format.
   (c) Vendor (service bureau) shall do all filming, processing, duplicating and inspection, and shall box processed film and prepare film carton labels as specified.
   (d) Filming shall be done on customer's premises by personnel

101

cleared for secret work.*

(e) Film processing shall be done on vendor's premises by personnel cleared for secret work.*

(f) Camera targets and carton labels will be provided by customer.

2. COM (Magnetic Tape Input)

(a) Digital data base will consist of the equivalent of some 500,000 pages of alphanumeric data, with an estimated average of 1500 characters per page at the normal 132/60 density.†

(b) Data will be contained on 9-track tape with a packing density of 1600 bpi.‡

(c) Pages shall be reproduced in "comic" format on 16mm roll film at equivalent 24X reduction.

(d) Vendor (service bureau) shall do all COM-generating, processing, duplicating and inspection of film, and shall box processed film and prepare film carton labels as specified.

(e) All work shall be done on vendor's premises by personnel cleared for secret work.*

(f) Vendor shall provide, as the end product, one complete camera master microform file, plus one complete contact duplicate file on vesicular film (negative-appearing images), and shall return input magnetic tape along with output microforms.

3. Items Applicable to Both Source Document and COM Situations.

(Both situations may have certain common requirements. These are examples.)

(a) Work shall commence on or about [date], and shall be completed within approximately [ ]** days therefrom.

(b) Personnel, film, and all necessary equipment and miscellaneous supplies shall be provided by vendor.

(c) Except for the one duplicate microform file specified, vendor shall be forbidden to further duplicate or reproduce input data base or output microforms.

(d) Upon completion of work, vendor shall be responsible for safe delivery of finished microforms and original data base.

In addition, in a COM situation only, the customer may want to specify use of forms overlays, and, in the case of fiche output, will have to specify header content and characteristics (fields included, character size, how it is to be extracted, etc.). As previously mentioned, these and other technical matters are best clarified through preliminary discussions with prospective vendors. In both document and COM situations, the customer may additionally wish to specify such things as film type (manufacturer and product code) and quality requirements to be met in the output microforms.

---

*This may be impractical because of high employee turnover.

†132 characters per line; 60 lines per page, (based on 11 x 14-inch paper printout).

‡1600 bits per linear inch of tape

**In the particular example given, 120 days (about four months) would be reasonable for the source document situation, and 3 to 5 days for the COM.

TABLE C

Vendor (service bureau) cost estimates for the microfilming of a hypothetical 500,000 letter-size document pages, or the equivalent in digital data. Separate comparative estimates are shown for each of two input formats and each of three output formats. The estimates cover provision of a silver master plus a diazo or vesicular duplicate of each.

OUPUT FORMAT	VENDOR ESTIMATES FOR (INPUT FORMAT)		
	(SOURCE DOCUMENTS)		(DIGITAL DATA)
	CUSTOMER PREMISES	VENDOR PREMISES	VENDOR PREMISES
16 mm Rolls			
Vendor A	$19,000	$16,500	$ 4,500
Vendor B	26,000	22,000	5,500
Vendor C	-	50,000	6,500
16 mm CARTRIDGES			
Vendor A	$19,500	$17,000	$5,200
Vendor B	26,500	22,500	6,250
Vendor C	-	50,500	7,250
98-FR. FICHE (16 mm STRIP-UP)			
Vendor A	$22,000	$20,000	-
Vendor B	41,500	38,000	-
Vendor C	-	55,000	-
98-FR. FICHE (105 mm)			
Vendor A	$20,000	$18,500	$5,500
Vendor B	-	-	8,000
Vendor C	-	60,000	8,250

Note: Vendors A, B, and C for source document estimates are not necessarily the same as those for digital data (COM) estimates.

The figures shown in Table C will provide some guidance in estimating service bureau costs. They are quotations obtained by the author from three reputable service bureaus, in different parts of the country, for the filming and processing of a hypothetical data base of 500,000 letter-size document pages, in accordance with a set of specifications similar to the above. Separate estimates were obtained for source document and digital data inputs (the latter for COM output) and for each of three output formats. In the case of the COM approach, the 500,000 "pages" is based on the total number of separate film frames produced from the input data, which the service bureau receives in the form of COM-compatible magnetic tape.

As noted in the table, in all cases the estimates include one copy film duplicate of each silver master. This is common practice, particularly where all or part of the original data base will eventually be destroyed.

On a per-page basis, service bureau charges for filming and processing range anywhere from 2 1/2 to 10 cents for letter-size source documents on fiche or 16mm rolls. The wide range is attributable to variations both in geographic locations and in the size of the service bureau operation. For COM, the *maximum* charge (on a contract basis) works out to about a penny a frame, and, for both source documents *and* COM, fiche tends to lean more toward the higher end of the range than 16mm rolls in cost per frame. For the filming of larger documents (or grid arrays) on 35mm rolls, 10 to 12 cents a frame seems to be the current norm.

The charges given for 16mm and fiche—source documents *and* COM—are based on a 500,000-page job. For smaller jobs, they would be slightly higher. However, there is no simple correlation because some service bureaus have a minimum charge policy ($25 per job, for example). It is also difficult to define what constitutes a small, large, or average-size job.

For processing alone, the rates are fairly uniform from one vendor to another: $1.80 to $2.50 per 16mm roll (100-foot); $2 to $3 a roll for 35mm; and $5 to $10 for 105mm. Duplicating charges are even more consistent: about a quarter of a cent per frame for either fiche or 16mm roll (about 5 cents a foot for roll); 8 cents a foot for 35mm rolls; and 8 to 12 cents apiece for aperture cards. For the most part, these duplicating charges assume diazo or vesicular film. Silver duplication will generally run somewhat higher.

The charge for pick-up and delivery—of original documents, computer tapes, and the finished product—may be either absorbed in the total cost of a job or imposed on a per-trip basis. $10 a trip within a big city, and one trip a day, is probably typical. As for bringing in equipment and personnel to do a job on the customer's premises, one of the service bureaus queried quoted a flat extra charge of $25 a day. Others will add anywhere from 20 to 45 percent to the total cost of a job, and still others will simply not take a job that requires them to work outside their own premises.

One thing that these cost generalizations may not reflect is the possible added cost for various "nuisances" that may be encountered once the work is underway. For example, some of the original paper in the source document situation may be badly wrinkled or creased and may require special handing; some of it, by its nature, may have to be filmed on a planetary camera to ensure that it meets output quality requirements, in which case all associated documents would have to be included in order to keep the grouping intact. Although our specification describes the input documents as "loose, letter-size. . . " there may be some staples and fanfolds that have been overlooked. All of these things can add significantly to the cost, *and this is true, obviously, of both an in-house and outside vendor situation.* For a big job like this, the service bureau will usually have examined the data base before quoting, and will have allowed for such preparation costs in the quotation.

A cost that was not solicited from any of the service bureaus contacted, because it is not one of the normal services, is that for the production of so called "ultrafiche"—microfiche containing images reduced more than 90X. Just in case this route is being considered, it is well to know that production and updating can be expensive. One source quotes a production cost range of $600 to $900 *per master fiche.*

III. Filing and Retrieval Facilities

In a basic micrographic system, the filing facilities need be nothing more than a small cabinet of drawers. Whatever microform is used, the space re-

Fig. 8.1. Comparative space requirements of microfilm versus paper for a given quantity of information. The picture speaks for itself.

quired will be a tiny fraction of that required for the paper equivalent. (See Figure 8.1.) Total space requirements, however, will depend on the nature of the system. For example, if original paper documents must still be retained, there will obviously be a net gain in space requirements. This need not necessarily mean increased space *costs,* however, because the paper file will now rarely, if ever, have to be accessed and can therefore be relocated to space that is otherwise wasted: for example, a remote corner of an attic or basement. Or, for a modest continuing expenditure, it can be transferred to the custody of a commercial storage warehouse.

It is entirely possible that a net *saving* in space *costs* will be realized even where the original paper must be retained. But, realistically, space saving is usually a factor only in those cases where all or part of the original file can be destroyed. This includes duplicate paper files in a decentralized system, the destruction of which results in definite space savings at the satellite locations even though the master paper file may still be retained at the central point.

The size of the investment in micrographic storage and retrieval hardware is going to depend not only on the size of the file as initially converted from paper or magnetic tape, but also on the anticipated rates of usage, growth and updating. It will also depend to some extent on the microform that has been selected. If the pages are engineering drawings to be contained on single 35 mm frames in aperture cards, it is possible that the file will require as much as 100 times the space required for a fiche file of the same number of letter-size pages.

Generalized space requirements and costs for microform storage hardware (trays, drawer units, cabinets)

| 16 mm Roll or Cartridge— | | | Storage Hardware | |
Size of File (Document Pages)	Quantity of Rolls or Cartridges Req'd	Sq. Ft.	Height (Inches)	Approx. Cost
50,000	17-34	2.5	6	$ 25-$ 70
500,000	167-335	2.5	25-44	$100-$500
1000,000	334-670	2.5-6.0	44	$700-$6500
35 mm Roll— Size of File (Document Pages)				
50,000	89-125	5	12	$250
500,000	890-1250	5-13	50-58	$1300-$2000
1000,000	1780-2500	13-22	50-58	$2600-$3300
98-Frame Fiche— Size of File (Document Pages	Approx. QTY of Fiche Req'd			
5,000	52-100	0.25-1.12	5-15	$5-$95
50,000	511-1000	1.5-2.5	5	$5-$300
500,000	5,110-10,000	5	20-36	$300-$3500
1000,000	10,220-20,000	5-10	36-67	$3500-$5500
EAM Image Card— Size of File (Document Pages)	Approx. QTY of Cards Req'd			
5,000	5,000	2	5	$70
50,000	50,000	4	38-52	$350-$500
500,000	500,000	28-43	52	$3000-$4600
1000,000	1000,000	50-80	52	$5800-$9500

For a file with a comparatively low usage rate, relatively inexpensive cabinets of drawers will probably suffice. At higher usage rates, mechanized rotary files or automated retrieval systems may be required to minimize queuing delays. In some cases of high usage rate—again, depending on the nature of the system—it may be necessary to maintain several duplicates of the master file so that the same documents can be accessed simultaneously at multiple stations.

Tables D and E show representative space requirements and costs for storage and retrieval hardware. They are based on the following source document page capacities per unit carrier for a particular microform:

MICROFORM	NUMBER OF SOURCE DOCUMENT PAPERS PER UNIT CARRIER
16mm roll or cartridge	1500—3000
35mm roll or cartridge	400—565
4x6'' microfiche	50—98
EAM image card	1

All the above capacities assume a single image per frame, and those for the roll and fiche formats assume the images to be arranged in "comic" fashion. (See Chapter 1). The lower limit of the capacity ranges for rolls and cartridges assumes use of discrete optical retrieval coding between frames, one code "patch" per frame. For 16mm, these patches (or patterns) were estimated to be about the same size as an image frame, and, for 35mm, they were estimated to be about half the size of an image frame. Actually, 35mm roll film is less likely to contain between-frames coding. But, in any event, these figures will serve as fair estimates of the minimum number of frames likely to be contained on a 100-foot roll of film. The high limit of the capacity ranges for rolls and cartridges is the maximum number of frames containable under normal conditions. For 35mm, it assumes a 2-inch interval ("pull-down") between frames, that is, a distance of two inches from the center of one frame to the center of the next.

For fiche, the low limit of 50 is an arbitrary average number of frames per unit carrier, whereas the high limit of 98 is the maximum number containable within the standard fiche grid configuration.

The single number 1 for EAM image cards assumes an engineering drawing system, or similar "unit" system, in which there is never more than one document page image per card. Actually, in some engineering drawing

TABLE E

Generalized space requirements and costs for automated microform-retrieval units offering integral storage of the microform file (or a segment thereof).

MICROFORM	Approximate Page Capacity Ranges of Available systems	Approx. Size		Approximate Cost ($)
		Square Feet	Height (inches)	
16mm Roll	5,000 or less (single cartridge)	3-3.5	23-29	2,000-8,000
	1,000,000 and up	9.5	60	18,000-20,000
35mm Roll	500-9,000	5-7	48	4,800- 6,000
Fiche	5,000 or less (single cartridge)	3-3.5	20	2,000- 3,000
	50,000 to 75,000	5	19	4,300-5,200
	100,000 to 500,000 (semi-automated)	5-15	8-10	5,000-12,000 (avg.: 9,000)
	1,000,000 and up (semi- or fully auto)	5-20	20-96	7,000-150,000 (avg.: 60,000)
Image Cards (semi-automated retrieval un- less other- wise noted)	5,000 or less	5-8	8-10	5,000-12,000
	6,000 to 12,000	5-15	8-30	8,000-15,000 (avg.: 10,000)
	100,000 and up (semi- or fully auto)	20-27	84-96	30,000-150,000 (avg.: 85,000)
105mm Scroll	100,000 or less	16	50	6,000-8,300
Ultrafiche	90,000 to 120,000	2	22	4,000-6,000

Note: average prices are shown only where the range is particularly wide. Where no average is shown, it is either because the range is not sufficiently wide to warrant it, or because the equipment is generally available only at prices at or near the extremes shown.

systems, a single large drawing sheet can be sectionalized and distributed among two or more cards, which would mean an average of *less* than one page image per card.

The tables assume only *one* working file, and the space and cost figures shown allow for file growth on an incremental basis. That is, if the quantity of unit carriers required will just about fill two trays or drawers, the space and cost figures will be for three such units rather than two. In Table E, the actual commercial units on which the sizes and costs are based are automated retrieval units capable of containing complete files, in microform (within the capacity limits shown), on a stand-alone basis.

Bear in mind that with automated retrieval there are going to be extra costs associated with encoding of the microform. Accessory equipment for the purpose is covered under *Miscellaneous Items* at the end of this chapter. In addition, some systems may require the addition of a special coding strip or clip to each unit microform. Typically these will cost 10 to 15 cents each, precoded by a service bureau. Optical encoding may, in some cases, be an integral camera capabilility, the cost for which will be reflected in the camera price. Retrieval coding of COM-generated film (typically *image count)* will usually be a function of the program required for computer output of COM-compatible tapes.

Bear in mind also that full automation will not absolutely ensure faster retrieval in all cases. Its sole advantage may be the greater file integrity and security it provides, in which case it is on that basis that it must be justified, economically or otherwise. Moreover, automation means increased complexity, which invariably means greater and more specialized maintenance activity—an additional cost factor to consider.

One additional cost element that warrants a brief look in connection with the retrieval of microimages is that of *remote* retrieval. There are actually two costs to consider: (1) that of the *terminal,* including installation and maintenance, and (2) *transmission* costs.

As noted in Chapter 5, there are basically two ways to access a file remotely. One is by *TV,* and the other by *facsimile* or *fax.* It could conceivably also be accessed via a straight digital data system with a human interface, but this would be makeshift and not normally desirable. It was also noted in Chapter 5 that fax terminal equipment capable of accepting microform input is not widely available and is therefore costly. The more important cost, however, is that of transmission, and it is here that fax has a decided edge over closed-circuit TV, except possibly for systems confined to "in-house" operations. Fax can transmit for long distances over ordinary telephone circuits, whereas TV requires special broadband channels.

Typical current costs and space requirements for remote accessing terminal equipment are shown in Table F. For the fax configurations, the size information applies to both the send and receive terminals (separately). In all cases, the fax receiver is a more or less conventional unit that outputs paper of essentially the same size as the original document before microfilming. The speed of these systems in minutes per frame assumes that the microimage is of a letter-size document.

The two fax systems marked by asterisks use special *digital data compression* techniques to achieve a measure of redundancy reduction and

Generalized space requirements and costs for remote accessing terminal equipment.

Note: Some of this equipment is not necessarily commercially available, and costs shown are therefore strictly conjectural. Equipment in this category is identified by an asterisk (*).

Terminal Description	Type of Transmission Facility	Minutes Per Frame	Approx. Size		Approx. Terminal Cost	
			Sq. Ft.	Height (Inches)	Send	Receive
Fax Transmitter, 16mm Cartridge Input	Telephone or Wideband	1-8	2.5	50	$20,000	9,000
*Fax Transmitter, Various Micro-Form Inputs	Telephone	0.5-2	5	52	14,000	12,000
*Fax Transmitter, Microfiche Input	Telephone	1-2	5	52	10,000	10,000
Fax Transmitter, EAM Image Card Input	Telephone or Wideband	1-8	5	52	10,000	10,000
CCTV Camera, Lensed for Microimage Reading	Video	Instant.	-	-	4,000	2,000
*CCTV System For Fiche & Image Card Inputs	Video	Instant.	-	-	$14,000	
CCTV System For Fiche & Image Card Inputs	Video	Instant.	-	-	20,000	
SSTV System, Variable Speed	Telephone To Video	0.01-1	-	-	15,000	

thus enable higher-than-normal transmission speeds over voice-grade (telephone) circuits. The speeds shown for these systems assume transmission via the Direct Distance Dial (DDD) network at various resolutions. Higher speeds are possible on specially conditioned lines or with some of the new digital data services. Of the actual systems on which these two descriptions are loosely based, one is a successfully tested prototype, and the other is in the planning stage.

Depending on the trade-offs between resolution, speed, and transmission costs, the fax configurations can generally serve both *word-in-context* and *individual character identification* applications, regardless of document size. The TV systems, on the other hand, cannot reliably serve the latter without resort to a *zoom* capability. TV systems are generally incapable of scan resolutions much beyond 2000 lines per frame. For a letter-size document, this would be more than adequate in most cases. However, for an 11x17 inch engineering drawing reproduced in its entirety on the CRT screen, it begins to be marginal.

With appropriate accessory electronics, all of these systems are capable of *broadcast* operation, i.e., a single transmitter serving multiple receivers. Typically, the additional purchase cost involved for this capability would

Generalized transmission costs associated with remote accessing of microform files via fax and slow-scan TV.

Note: "All-digital" service is not yet widely available as of the time of writing.

Type of Service	Approximate Usage Charge (Per Month, Unless Otherwise Noted.)			Additional Monthly Charges Per Trmnl (Approx.)	Instal. Per Trmnl (One-Time) (Approx.)
	50 Miles	500 Miles	1500 Miles		
Direct Distance Dial Telephone: (a) Day Rate*	$0.15/ min.	$0.34/ min.	$0.44/ min.	$10-$14	$20-$30
(b) Night Rate*	$0.10/ min.	$0.16/ min.	$0.21/ min.		
Voice-Grade (4 kHz) Leased Line, C2 Conditioning	$130	$1200	$2000	$53	$50
Wideband (48 kHz) Leased Line	$750	$6350	$14,000	$425	$200
"All-Digital" Service (a) 2400 Bps	$20-$40	$200-$400	$600-$1150	$85-$125	$125-$150
(b) 4800 Bps	$30-$45	$300-$450	$900-$1350	$135-$165	$125-$200
(c) 9600 Bps	$45-$65	$450-$650	$1350-$1950	$185-$205	$125-$200
(d) 56,000 Bps	$200-$300	$2000-$3000	$6000-$9000	$345-$395	$175

range between $3000 and $5000 per send terminal for a 10-station simultaneous-receive capability via voice-grade leased lines.

Table G provides a very general picture of the transmission costs associated with remote accessing via fax and slow-scan TV. The cost of video channels for CCTV is not covered because of the inherent impracticality of using this medium in anything beyond an "in-house" configuration. "In-house" may be interpreted to include the linking of buildings within a complex, such as a campus or large factory. In any event, it will normally involve installation of *coaxial cable* by a qualified contractor, the cost of which will vary widely. Private microwave is, of course, an alternative possibility.

The additional monthly charges and installation charge shown in the table for the DDD network include the required Data Access Arrangement (DAA), furnished by the phone company, and assume no existing phone. If the DAA is being added to an existing phone, deduct $15 to $20 from the installation cost and $6 to $8 from the additional monthly charges shown in the table.

IV. Duplicating and Distribution

Duplicating, like filming and processing, is often entrusted to an outside service bureau. This, of course, does not include *demand* duplication of unit microforms as a local service to file users. The need for maximum security of file content may also be a factor in whether the duplication is done in-house or outside. Bear in mind that the term *duplication* generally implies *contact printing* of *copy microforms* from the master. It does not include reproduction of hard copy from microimages, although, in some cases, this task, too, can be consigned to a service bureau.

Table H shows some typical unit costs for duplication of microforms by a service bureau. Note that the microform shown is that in which the duplicates are produced, but not necessarily that in which the masters are sub-

TABLE H

Typical unit costs for duplication of microforms by a service bureau, based on average of solicited quotations.

MICROFORM	APPROX. COST PER DUPLICATE UNIT CARRIER*		
	SILVER	DIAZO	VESICULAR
16mm Roll (100 ft.)	$7	$5	$4.50
35mm Roll (100 ft.)	$9	$7	$7
Microfiche, 4x6", 98-Fr. (from 105mm fiche masters)	$0.50 ($0.20 to $1.00)	$0.15	$0.15
EAM Image Cards		$0.12	$0.12

*by "unit carrier" is meant a single roll, single fiche, or single card. The costs shown cover only a single generation duplication—i.e. they do not cover the two-step duplication that may be required in some cases to ensure a given image polarity.

Note: For an estimate of the cost per frame, in a typical source document microfilming situation, divide the above costs by the number of pages per unit carrier shown on page 106.

mitted to the service bureau. Costs are shown for each of the three basic types of duplicating film—silver, diazo, and vesicular. Generally speaking, the duplication of documents in microform, particularly on a quantity basis, is less costly than paper-to-paper reproduction.

Tables I and J show representative equipment and film costs, and space and throughput data relating to in-house contact duplication of microforms. The throughput speeds given in Table I are important in determining the number of separate units required for a given anticipated level of duplicating activity. Not covered in Table J are the copy cards that will be required for duplication purposes in an aperture card system. (Copy cards are aperture cards containing unexposed copy film). These currently sell for between $13 and $27 per thousand, depending on the quantity purchased.

TABLE I

Generalized throughput speeds, space requirements and costs for contact microform duplicating equipment.

MODE; THROUGHPUT RANGES	APPROX. SIZE		APPROXIMATE COST ($)
	SQ.FT.	HEIGHT (Inches)	
ROLL-TO-ROLL			
(a) Low Vol. (under 500 ft/hr)	2-6	19-42	5500-8000
(b) Med. Vol. (500-5000 ft/hr)	3-8	22-68	5500-20,000 (avg.: 10,000)
(c) Hi. Vol. (over 5000 ft/hr)	3-15	19-75	4500-75,000 (avg.: 15,000)
FICHE-TO-FICHE			
(a) Low Vol. (under 500/hr)	1-6	8-46	650-12,000 (avg.: 3000)
(b) Med/Hi Vol. (500/hr and up)	3-13	22-51	2100-27,000 (avg.: 13,000)
CARD-TO-CARD			
(a) Low Vol. (under 500/hr)	2-4	7-48	1200-4000
(b) Med/Hi Vol. (500/hr and up)	3-10	11-52	3300-65,000 (avg.: 20,000)

NOTE: Average prices are shown only where the range is particularly wide.

Representative costs of copy film for contact microform duplication

Film Width	Approximate Cost Per 100 Feet		
	Diazo Type	Vesicular Type	Silver "Print" Type
16 mm	$0.80- 1.00	$0.80-1.20	$1.25- 1.80
35 mm	1.50-$2.00	$2.00-3.00	$2.25-$3.50
105 mm	$5.00-10.00*	$7.50-9.50	9.50-12.00

*High price for 105 mm assumes inclusion of header striping.

An additional cost where diazo copy film is used is that of the ammonia required for image development.Vesicular film is developed by application of heat. Unfortunately, it is an extremely difficult cost to nail down with any accuracy, for several reasons, chief among which are the following:

(a) both the design of the particular machine and the production volume have a bearing on the amount of ammonia consumed;

(b) purchase prices tend to vary widely on a geographic basis and on the basis of the "quality" rating of the gas purchased;

(c) the consumption rate in a given situation is generally adjusted to obtain the optimum balance between assurance of complete image development and avoidance of fume problems;

(d) the quantity of ammonia required for proper development may vary with the brand or specific type of diazo film.

The author has been quoted consumption rates as low as one pound (approx. 23 cubic feet) of gaseous ammonia per 60,000 fiche and as high as one pound per 10,000 aperture cards (roughly the equivalent of 800 fiche in terms of image area). If it were valid to do so, this would interpret to a range of about 2500 to nearly 200,000 feet of 16mm roll film per pound of ammonia. However, a more practical estimate for roll film might be from 5000 to 20,000 feet per pound.

As for commercial price, on a continuing cylinder refill basis, a pound of gaseous ammonia can range from less than a dollar to perhaps as much as $35, depending on the terms of purchase, quantities involved, quality rating, etc. Thus, *at the very worst,* ammonia consumption may add a couple of cents to the cost of producing one fiche duplicate, or something less than a penny per foot of 16mm or 35mm roll film. At the opposite extreme, the cost per unit carrier would be negligible. On the average, therefore, we are talking about a cost of a fraction of a penny per fiche or EAM image card, and well under half a dollar per 100 feet of 16mm or 35mm roll film.

This brings us to *distribution* costs, and it is sufficient to say that several hundred pages in microfiche form can be mailed First Class for the price of a single postage stamp. The equivalent number of pages in original paper form would cost several dollars to mail First Class, and, even at third class bulk rate (currently 32 cents a pound), would still cost more than fiche at first class. In other words, for these same alternatives to be equal in cost-

TABLE K

Comparison of mailing weights, fiche versus paper

| Form | Quantity of Physical Pieces Per Maximum Allowable Weight For Base Rate in Class* | | |
	Per oz. (1st Class)	Per lb. (3rd Class-Bulk)	Per 2 lbs. (4th Class-Parcel)†
4x6" Microfiche:			
(a) "bare"	6	105	210
(b) in protective paper pockets	3	60	120
8 1/2 x 11" paper:			
(a) SUB 16	7	115	230
(b) SUB 20	5	95	190

* Reasonable allowances are made for envelopes or wrappings in each case.

† Postage is determined by zone, but an overall average for a max. 2-lb. parcel as of January, 1975, would be about $1.00.

per-page, even under relatively unfavorable conditions for fiche, i.e., no more than three fiche per ounce at First Class, and as many as 115 paper pages per pound at Third Class Bulk, the average unit fiche in the package would have to contain no more than 12 images. (3x3 fiche = 3 ounces = $0.30; 115 paper pages = 1 pound = $0.32.) Table K gives the basic weight/class comparisons.

V. Display and Reproduction Equipment

Filming, processing and duplicating can all be left to service bureaus,

TABLE L

Representative prices for various types of microform readers

MICROFORM	"LAP" AND PORTABLE*	DESK-TOP		CENTRAL REFERENCE ("LARGE-SCREEN")
		SMALL SCREEN*	LARGE SCREEN	
Roll† 16mm	approx. $250	-	$400-1500 (avg.: $800)	-
35 mm	approx. $250	-	-	approx. $700
Both	-	approx. $400	$400-2100 (avg.: $1400)	$1000-1300
Cartridge, Cassette	approx. $600	-	$190-1500 (avg.: $900)	$550-1700 (avg.: $1000)
Fiche/Jacket	$25-250 (avg.: $125)	$100-200	$85-650 (avg.: $260)	$300-800 (avg.: $550)
EAM Image Card	$100-400 (avg.: $225)	$100-325 (avg.: $170)	$75-950 (avg.: $300)	$725-1000
Ultrafiche	approx. $450	$200-325	$300-525 (avg.: $400)	$2000-3000
Micro-Opaque	-	approx. $400		approx. $600
Multimedia	$200-250	-	$375-2700 (avg.: $1400)	$1300-1500

PROJECTORS, FOR VARIOUS MICROFORMS (no built-in screen): $85-300 (avg.: $160)

---

* These may not display an image in its entirety. ("small screen" includes 8 1/2 x 11 inches and smaller.)
† The higher prices in this category are for motor-driven readers.
Note: Average prices are shown only where the range is particularly wide.

but even the most basic active micrographic system requires the purchase or rental of at least one device for enlarging the microimages to eye-readable size. That device can be a reader, reader-printer, or enlarger-printer. Typically there will be more than one, and they may be of a single type (e.g., just readers) or a mix of all three. The system parameters will determine the specific need.

Tables L and M show the general types of units available for the more common microforms, with representative costs. Enlarger-printers differ from reader-printers in that they do not offer a display capability, *per se*. Of the two, enlarger-printers are in the minority and are generally confined to use in production or other high volume printing situations.

As for the size of these devices and the required space, the portable, or so-called "lap" readers can range from less than 1/2 to 2 square feet at the base and from 2-1/2 inches to about 19 inches in height. The extremes of the height range will usually apply to collapsible type portables. Screen

TABLE M

Representative Space Requirements And Prices For Microform Reader-Printers And Enlarger-Printers

Microform	READER-PRINTERS SMALL/MED.			READER-PRINTER LARGE			ENLARGER-PRINTER		
	SIZE		APPROX. COST ($)	SIZE		APPROX. COST ($)	SIZE		APPROX. COST ($)
	SQ.FT.	HT.(")		SQ.FT.	HT.(")		SQ.FT.	HT.(")	
Roll, 16mm only	3-4	27-30	1300-2000				18	40-45	5000 or 250/mo.
Roll, 35mm only	-	-	-				7-15	55-70	15,000 or 160 to 225/mo.
Roll, 16/35mm	3-5	30-32	1500-3000						
Cartridge	3-7	19-32	1300-3200	12	50	8000			
Fiche/Jacket	2-7	20-53	500-4000 (avg.:1750)				4-15	40-62	2000-19,000 (avg.:10,000) or 225 to 1500/mo.
Image Card	3-7	24-53	750-4000 (avg.:1700)	8-25	33-54	2600-8500 (avg.:5600)	4-66	39-84	2000-50,000 (avg.:18,000) or 160 to 550/mo.

Note: Average prices are shown only where the range is particularly wide.

size for the portables may range from 4x5 inches to as much as 11x13 inches, or even larger. Desk-top readers will generally occupy from 1 square foot or less to about 3 square feet of space; may stand as high as 2 feet; and may have screens as large as 14x20 inches. Central reference, or so-called "large-screen" readers may be of table-top or console design; may require anywhere from 4 to 10 square feet of table or floor space, and may have screens ranging from 11x19 to 24x36 inches or larger in size, depending on the application.

Typical sizes of reader-printers and enlarger-printers are given in Table M, along with representative prices.

It is well to know some of the capabilities obtained for the money expended for display and reproduction equipment, and whether they are within or beyond the basic requirements for the system being considered. As noted in Table L, for example, some of the more compact readers may not display an image in its entirety. The reason is that a compromise must be struck between screen-size and adequate magnification. Conversely, some "large screen" fiche readers are capable of displaying two images on the screen simultaneously. It is also well to keep in mind that the capabilities of readers and reader-printers in general overlap those of automated retrieval units having display and print capabilities. Inclusion of these latter devices in the list of required equipment for a system may reduce the need for separate readers and reader-printers.

Another economic factor specifically concerning the print capability is the cost of materials consumed in the production of hard copy. Obviously the principal material is paper. For most processes, there are also chemical costs, but, except for very high print volumes, these are generally negligible. Table N provides some guidelines on material cost per print.

TABLE N

Generalized material costs associated with use of reader-printers.

PRINT SIZE	MATERIAL COST PER PRINT ($)*		
	ELECTROSTATIC	DRY SILVER	ELECTROLYTIC
8-1/2 x 11-inch square foot	0.04 - 0.05 0.05 - 0.08	0.06 - 0.07† 0.08 - 0.09	0.11 - 0.14 0.15 - 0.20

*Based on use of roll paper unless otherwise noted.
†8-1/2 x 11-inch cut sheets cost approximately 10-1/2 cents each.

Table L excludes one type of viewing device that does not quite qualify as a reader. It is a hand-held viewer for fiche, jackets or aperture cards. In its simplest configuration, it is merely "aimed" at an existing light source while being held to the eye. Other versions have built-in illumination. Depending on the degree of sophistication, these retail for anywhere from $5 to $80.

VI. Miscellaneous Items

For most micrographic systems, there will be certain miscellaneous items required to complete the system's equipment and apparatus needs. Depending on the nature of the system, and on what tasks, if any, are per-

Representative space requirements and prices for miscellaneous items.

ITEM	SIZE		Approx. Cost ($)
	Sq. Ft.*	Height (")	
Roll Film Rewinds (PR.)	-	-	35-45
Film Splicers—			
1. Tape	-	-	15-30
2. Straight Cement	-	-	50-85
3. Hot Cement	-	-	800-1300
4. Ultrasonic	-	-	1500-2100
Densitometer	-	-	95-1600 (avg: 850)
Microscope	-	-	50-500 (avg: 200)
"Inspection Station"			
(Rewind/splicer, Re-			
wind/viewer, etc.)	1-10	6-36	150-6000
			(avg: 500-1000)
Cartridge Loader	1.5-3	6-12	150-700
Jacket Filler	-	-	150-750
(with viewer)	1.5-3	20-25	1200-4500
Fiche Strip-Up App.	1-2	6-12	1100-2000
Fiche Cutter (105mm)	1.5-3	6-14	1800-6000
			(avg: 4000)
Fiche Retrieval Clip	-	-	850
Attacher/Notcher			
Mounter, Film-to	1-8	5-50	300-5500
Aperture card			(avg: 1500)
EAM Interpreting Card			
Punch (80-80)	7.5	39	60-120/month
EAM Keypunch			
Reproducer	9	50	125-150/month
Automatic Stack-Load			
EAM Interpreter	9	46	185-325/month

NOTE: Average prices are shown only where the range is particularly wide.

*Absence of entry indicates space requirement of less than one square foot.

formed by a service bureau, these could add appreciably to the total initial expenditure and, in some cases, to the continuing costs. For an EAM aperture card system, for example, there may be need for precision mounters and possibly for some dedicated keypunching and interpreting equipment. For a jacket or fiche system there may be need for jacket-filling and stripping-up apparatus. For systems in which filming and processing will be done on-premises by the user, there will be some minimal need for inspection apparatus to ensure quality control.

Table O shows a representative sampling of the kinds of miscellaneous items that may be required, together with approximate space requirements and costs.

One other cost that bears mentioning, and that applies only to computer-related systems, is *software.* Software costs, to design and "debug" the computer program, can be a substantial portion of the total cost to implement a system. The components are *programmer time* and *computer time,* of which several man-months of the former and many hours of the latter could conceivably be consumed in the process of implementing a system. Naturally, the more specialized the program and the more unique it is to a specific user, the more costly it will be.

The best that can be said in the way of guidance on software costs is that, to the extent that it is possible or practical to do so, the system should be designed around the use of available (off-the-shelf) programs. In practically all cases where either a computer-related micrographic system

117

configuration or a specific task that involves computer use is put out for competitive bidding, software will be included as a component of the vendor's quotation.

*　　*　　*

These, then, are the many elements that collectively determine the economics of a micrographic system. The next chapter will cover component selection and system design. It will show how the various costs discussed in this chapter can be optimized by judicious selection of system elements to meet specific end requirements.

Suggested Additional Reading

Ballou, Hubbard W., ed., *Guide to Micrographic Equipment.* Vol. I, Production Equipment, 256p.; Vol. II, User Equipment, 216p.; Vol. III, COM Recorders, 80p. Silver Spring, Md.: NMA, 1975.

Floyd, Howard A., "Use Microfilm for Profit." *Reproductions Review and Methods,* May 1974. pp.18, 31.

Gratt, Eugene L., and W. Grant Ireson, *Principles of Engineering Economy.* 5th. edition. New York, N.Y.: Ronald Press, 1970. 640 p.

Kish, Joseph L., Jr., "Costing a COM Application." *Business Graphics,* November 1974. p.32.

Putnam, Dean H., "The Do-or-Buy Decision: In-House versus Contractual Microfilm Service." *The Journal of Micrographics,* Spring 1970. pp.103-105.

Chapter 9

Component Selection and System Design

Having determined whether our particular records-handling situation is, in fact, a candidate for micrographics (chapter 7), and having assessed the economics of adopting a micrographic system (chapter 8), we are ready to proceed with the selection of components for a specific system configuration. However, it is not the aim of this chapter, nor of this book for that matter, to take the dogmatic "how to" approach, providing rigid step-by-step instructions on system design. Rather its approach is, in effect, to provide the constants and let the reader "plug-in" his own variables.

Much of what will be said in this chapter may sound familiar, and that is because it probably will have been mentioned elsewhere in the book in one context or another. While this will serve as a review, the objective is to bring these scattered pieces into perspective to help in evolving a specific system plan.

I. Selecting the Microform

A logical first step in the planning of a micrographic system is to decide which of the several available microforms the system is to be based on. Among the considerations that should influence that decision are:
1. the degree of unitization appropriate to the type of material involved;
2. automation considerations, such as coding methods and integral storage within a retrieval device;
3. the anticipated production and duplication volumes;
4. distribution considerations;
5. equipment and material requirements;
6. the level of output quality required.

Let's briefly examine each of these.

1. Degree of Unitization

The desired degree of unitization, i.e., the number of page images per unit carrier, will depend largely on the extent to which individual pages are likely to be revised. As was pointed out in an earlier chapter, a disadvantage of "Collective", or multi-image, microforms is that if one or two pages of a rather lengthy document have to be revised, *all* of the pages of the affected unit carrier will usually have to be refilmed so that a complete new unit can replace the previous one. Thus, while one might hesitate to use microfiche for engineering drawings, for example, it might be the natural choice for microfilming periodicals, which, once published, will not be changed. A good illustration of this point is the Defense Department's recent decision to abandon the "8-up" aperture card format (eight images to a card-mounted 35 mm frame) in its microfilming of engineering specifications. Because of the high activity in single sheet reissues, the DOD has deemed it more economical to carry a single letter-size page per card.

This characteristic limitation of multi-image formats was recently made somewhat less restricting by the introduction of a new technology utilizing a transparent photoconductor (TPC) as the microform base, and thus permitting new images to be added to an existing master microform by an electrostatic process. The new image can *replace* a previous one by the simple expedient of using the same process to superimpose a *void* notice on the image of the page that has been revised. The use of the technique assumes that there will usually be space available on a fiche for the added images, and that it is acceptable for the revised pages to be out of their normal sequence.

2. Automation Considerations

All microforms are adaptable, one way or another, to fully automated retrieval. But, both the microform itself and the data base characteristics will determine which one lends itself best to a given situation. Table A gives some basic comparisons that will help in selecting the appropriate microform from the automation standpoint. Both semi- and fully automated retrieval are covered.

Some of the terminology used in the table may need clarifying. The term "standard reductions" for fiche and micro-opaques, for example, is meant to include the range from roughly 18X to 48X, but with the emphasis at the lower end of that range. For "high-reduction" fiche (above 48X), mention is made of *multiple film plane techniques* and *integral positional locating*. The first of these generally applies to so-called "ultrafiche" (reductions of 90X or more), and pertains to the recording of separate images at two focal planes, the front and rear of a relatively thick plastic sheet, for example, so that the mechanism can be arranged to "focus through" to the selected plane. The defocusing of intervening images renders them virtually invisible. The second of the two terms pertains to a technique that is common to virtually all automated fiche systems, but the importance of which becomes most evident at higher reductions, namely, the automatic locating of specific images by purely mechanical vertical and lateral movement of the microform carriage in degrees determined by the keyed-in search code. In other words, there need be no sensing of retrieval "marks" of any kind in order to locate an image.

TABLE A

Relative adaptability of various microforms to the automated retrieval of specific images.

MICROFORM	ADVANTAGES	LIMITATIONS
ROLL FILM	ideal for fully automated retrieval *where entire data base can be confined to single roll and will remain relatively static.* *	not particularly suitable if data base is subject to frequent change, unless separate reference to addenda can be tolerated.
	Good for *semi*automated retrieval, in cartridge or cassette form, where data base must be spread over multiple rolls.	Will normally require some form of optical coding at time of filming. Existing roll film is not readily adaptable.
	Design of retrieval device can be relatively simple.	Depending on retrieval scheme, size of rolls, and position of image on roll, retrieval time may widely vary.
FICHE, MICRO-OPAQUES, STANDARD REDUCTIONS	generally more suitable than roll film for *fully* automated retrieval from a comparatively large data base.	may require physical alteration for retrieval coding.
	existing fiche generally adaptable to fully automated retrieval.	Mechanical design of retrieval device generally more complex than for single-roll system.
	Can tolerate higher frequency of change than rolls, because of segmentation of file.	
	less variation in retrieval time per image.	
FICHE, HIGH REDUCTION	particularly suitable for *fully* automated retrieval (or *semi*automated with special cartridges) from a comparatively large data base where *compactness* is important.	not particularly suitable if data base is subject to frequent change, unless separate reference to addenda can be tolerated.
	less variable image retrieval time than for roll film.	production and updating of microforms may be a comparatively involved procedure.
	can utilize multiple film plane techniques to maximize image packing densities.	requires comparatively critical design of retrieval device.
	Can utilize integral positional locating to simplify search logic.	
EAM IMAGE CARDS	particularly suitable for semi-automated retrieval from a data base that is subject to frequent change.	For even a moderate size data base, retrieval unit will be comparatively large.
	existing cards generally adaptable to automated retrieval.	existing Hollerith keypunching cannot normally be used for retrieval purposes; cards will generally require physical alteration for retrieval coding.
		Task of selecting separate card per image may require relatively high mechanical complexity.

*The italicized qualification should not be taken to imply that fully automated retrieval from *multiple* rolls is necessarily impractical. There is at least one commercially available system in which this capability is achieved quite effectively.

121

3. Production and Duplication Volumes

Apart from variations in cost-per-image, there is no substantial reason for anticipated production volume to influence the choice of one microform over another. It is well to realize, however, that the cost-per-image for 35mm roll film, for example, can be three to four times that for 16mm*, and that, as pointed out in the previous chapter, the cost of ultrafiche production can be quite high. The latter is still a somewhat nonstandard microform, the production of which must normally be left to a service bureau because of the highly specialized equipment involved. Unfortunately, there are relatively few service bureaus equipped to handle ultrafiche.

Cost-per-image is less a factor in duplication than in production, although here there are possible savings to be realized with ultrafiche at very high duplication volumes. Its duplication cost-per-image can be five to ten times less than that of some of the more standard microforms. Duplication cost, on the other hand, can be a *negative* factor in the selection of another relatively nonstandard microform, the micro-opaque. As previously pointed out, the nature of this microform can make duplication a complex and expensive, if not impossible, proposition.

There are really two separate categories of duplication: (1) *bulk* (or *production)* duplication for distribution purposes, and (2) *demand* duplication of individual unit carriers to satisfy user requests at the file. What has been said so far of duplication costs as a factor in microform selection applies in general to both categories. However, demand duplication of ultrafiche and micro-opaques will not be a normal capability of any system using these somewhat special microforms. Similarly, a system in which rolls or cartridges are the end microform cannot feasibly offer demand duplication as a system capability. The reason is fairly obvious: the user will generally only want duplicates of certain frames or groups of frames. Even if the system were geared to providing selective strips of duplicate film on demand, and unless these were subsequently inserted in jackets, which could be a costly task on a demand basis, special readers would probably be required to permit practical use of such duplicates.

This pretty much leaves only jackets, standard fiche, and EAM aperture cards as the master microforms to be selected where demand duplication at the file will be a system requirement. Of these, the ability of jackets and fiche to permit duplication of large numbers of page images simultaneously could be a factor in the selection. But this will, of course, depend on the nature of the data base and how it is used. If, for example, the normal need is for duplicates of individual pages, this capability could prove wasteful on a demand duplication basis.

4. Distribution Considerations

Whatever has already been said about bulk duplication of master microforms is applicable as a distribution consideration. The other aspect of distribution is the cost of handling and mailing, and to try to decide which microform is the most economical in this respect can be a complicated task. This is revealed in Table B, which shows several interesting things of

---

*This assumes that the 35mm route was chosen either to permit filming larger documents or to film letter-size documents at a lower reduction, in either case only a single document being filmed per frame.

Comparative image quantities per unit weight for various microforms, relative to distribution by First Class mail.

IMAGE QUANTITIES VS. WEIGHT		MICROFORM				
		16mm, CART-RIDGE	100-FT. REEL	35mm, 100 FT. REEL†	98-FRAME FICHE	EAM IMAGE CARDS
LETTER-SIZE PAGES	MED.	2250	2250	2500	50	5
PER UNIT AT 24X	MAX.	3000	3000	4800	98	8
UNIT WEIGHT (OZ.)		6.00	3.65	7.70	0.143	0.083

*MAXIMUM QUANTITIES OF 24X LETTER-SIZE IMAGES WITHIN LIMITS OF 1ST CLASS POSTAL INCREMENTS (oz.) FOR MEDIAN AND MAXIMUM IMAGE QUANTITIES PER UNIT CARRIER**

OZ.	MED./MAX.	CARTRIDGE CASING, MAIL CARTON, & 6 FT. LDR/TRLR TOTAL 3.53 oz.	100-FT. REEL	35mm REEL	98-FRAME	EAM
1	MED.		REEL, BOX LDR/TRLR = 1.18 oz.	REEL, BOX LDR/TRLR = 1.90 oz.	150	45
1	MAX.				590	72
2	MED.		590	20	300	90
2	MAX.		770	35	1176	144
3	MED.		1355	395	500	135
3	MAX.		1770	755	1764	216
4	MED.	320	2120	770	650	180
4	MAX.	420	2770	1475	2352	288
5	MED.	1085	2250	1145	850	225
5	MAX.	1420	3000	2195	3038	360
6	MED.	1850	2685	1520	1050	270
6	MAX.	2420	3570	2915	3724	432
7	MED.	2250	3450	1895	1250	315
7	MAX.	3000	4570	3635	4410	504
8	MED.		4215	2270	1450	360
8	MAX.		5570	4355	5096	576
9	MED.		4500	2500	1650	405
9	MAX.		6000	4800	5782	648
10	MED.		4900	REEL, BOX, LDR/TRLR = 1.90 oz.	1800	450
10	MAX.		6400		6272	720

CARTRIDGE CASING, MAIL CARTON & 6 FT. LDR/TRLR TOTAL 3.53 oz.

Note: For approx. equivalent weight (in ounces) of actual pages on 20-weight paper, multiply any of the above image quantities by 0.16.

*Appropriate allowances are made for envelopes and cartons, including individual pockets for fiche. Quantities shown are for weights 0.05 oz. below indicated increment.

†These quantities assume maximum eight pages per frame (median: five).

varying significance.

The table makes incremental comparisons of image "packing densities" within a 10-ounce span for each of five microforms. The common denominator of all of the various weight/quantity relationships shown is that the microimage is consistently of a letter-size (8-1/2 x 11-inch) page, reduced 24X. In all cases, the images are assumed to be arranged to make most efficient use of the available space on the particular microform.

The differences in quantities of images mailable at a given weight for one microform versus another will be significant only in relatively high volume distribution situations. The more significant comparison is between the cost of distributing microforms and that of distributing the original paper. The saving in mail costs is generally substantial. (Table K of Chapter 8 compares mailing costs of paper at bulk and parcel rates with fiche at First Class.)

Nevertheless, let's take a moment to look at a couple of the comparisons that the table reveals. It is interesting, for example, that, at 10-ounce intervals, a 16mm cartridge, if mailed intact, will convey less than half the number of images transferable via plain reels for the same First Class postage cost. This is the penalty imposed by the extra weight of the cartridge housing. Obviously, the film alone can be mailed and inserted in the cartridge housing after receipt, in which case the image capacity will be about the same as that for film on reels.

Extra weight also works against the 35mm roll, which, despite its having at least double the image area, carries 25 to 50 percent fewer images than its own weight in 16mm rolls. A single, full, 100-foot 35mm roll, packaged for mailing weighs about 8.5 ounces, as compared with about half that amount for a full 16mm roll. The maximum quantity shown for the 16mm roll (at 10 ounces), incidentally, is for two full rolls plus part of a third. The bold dividers indicate the divisions between separate rolls.

Bear in mind that, for any of the five microforms in the table—fiche in particular—the quantities of images containable at a given weight can be substantially increased simply by going to a higher reduction.

5. Hardware and Material Requirements

The selection of a particular microform will, to some extent, govern the equipment and material needs of the system and, as in the case of production, duplication and distribution, the effects will be primarily economic. For example, a step-and-repeat camera for direct fiche production on 105mm film will cost roughly twice as much as a comparable 16mm or 35mm camera for roll film production. Similarly, selection of the 35mm aperture card as the system microform will impose additional material and hardware needs: besides the need for aperture cards and the possible need for a greater amount of film for a given number of documents, which will depend, of course, on the filming format, there will be a peripheral need for specially modified EAM card-handling equipment (keypunchers, interpreters, reproducers) and film-to-card mounters. In addition, the filing hardware requirement will be greater than for other microforms on an image-capacity basis.

Countering these added production costs for standard fiche and aperture cards is the fact that readers and reader-printers for these formats are, by nature, less expensive than those for roll film. It is a risky generalization to make, but, for two units roughly comparable in all other respects (e.g., screen size, level of illumination, etc.), the fiche or card unit can be expected to cost about 50 percent less than the roll film unit.

At higher reductions, these inherently "unitized" microforms (fiche and cards) offer still further advantages in the form of correspondingly lower material, file hardware, and space requirements.* But, as previously noted, any economic savings that might be realized in those areas are likely to be at least partially offset and perhaps even exceeded by higher production costs, particularly in the case of ultrafiche.

---

*This is generally true, of course, for roll type microforms as well. But the use of very high reductions has traditionally been confined to the more unitized formats, fiche in particular.

6. Output Quality Considerations

Selection of the microform can have a bearing on output quality in two ways:

(a) the limitation it places on the range of reductions;
(b) the possible relationship of the microform to the type of camera intended to be used.

The allowable range of reductions for a given page size is directly affected by the maximum frame size possible on the microform. Obviously, it is only the low end of the reduction range, the relative "largeness" of the microimage, that is limited. For example, an "E"-size engineering drawing (34" X 44") is customarily reduced 30X onto 35mm film, and, at that reduction, it fits the 35mm frame (roughly 1.21" x 1.63") with little margin to spare. To fit this same drawing on 16mm film, the minimum possible reduction would be about 66X. With currently available films and cameras, that would exceed the maximum allowable reduction for meeting accepted reproduction quality standards. Conversely, if 70mm film were used instead of 35mm, reductions as low as 15X would be possible for the same document, and accepted reproduction quality standards would undoubtedly be surpassed. In some engineering drawing systems, the original filming is done full-frame on 105mm film, the reason being to produce as perfect a first generation master as possible. From there, the working file masters are produced on 35mm film by precision optical printing from the 105mm camera negatives.

Although, theoretically, the low end of the reduction range for fiche should be quite flexible, anything less than 60 frames as the full complement will render the microform "nonstandard", and there may not be reproduction equipment available that can accommodate an image frame in its entirety. Even if existing equipment were adaptable (by a lens change, for example), the resulting reduced magnification might be insufficient to meet accepted readability standards.

As mentioned in Chapter 7, the degree of reduction can also affect readability when it is so high that it renders the images vulnerable to obliteration by dust particles or by microscopic imperfections in the emulsion. The effects of such impairments can be particularly devastating in a situation where the legibility of individual symbols or characters is essential, as in mathematical equations.

Item (b) (above) really concerns the choice of camera rather than the microform. But a link exists when roll film has been selected as an expedient to permit use of rotary cameras. Despite its many other merits, the rotary camera is generally not capable of as good resolution as a planetary camera in the same price category.

In the final analysis, it is really the nature of the data base that determines the level of output quality required. Once that has been determined, the foregoing considerations can be more aptly applied.

II. Microform Production Considerations

Camera selection has already been alluded to. It was pointed out, for example, the step-and-repeat cameras for fiche production from source documents tend to be more expensive than regular planetaries or rotaries, and that the output resolution from rotary cameras is generally less than that from planetaries at a given reduction. Thus we have two bases on which to select a camera. There are, in addition, combined camera-processors and COM devices to consider, and there are certain basic considerations regarding in-house processing. Let's briefly examine each of these points.

1. Fiche Production from Source Documents

Assuming that we have first decided on a particular microform, the comparatively higher price of step-and-repeat cameras will apply only if that microform happens to be fiche, and generally only if it is one of the accepted standard fiche formats, notably the NMA 98-frame grid. The alternative to the step-and-repeat camera for fiche production is, of course, the use of a 16mm roll film camera, with the output stripped-up into fiche masters. Considering that, except for maintenance, the purchase of a camera is essentially a one-time cost, the higher price of one type of camera over another could be a relatively insignificant factor, depending on production volume. The stripping-up of fiche masters from roll film imposes additional steps in the process, which—again, depending on production volume—could amount to an additional labor cost that might far outweigh the difference in camera prices.

But the choice might also be a purely practical matter, perhaps involving a dual output requirement. For example, it may be desired that less active documents remain in roll form for vault storage, while the more active ones are stripped-up as fiche. In an in-house operation it would almost certainly be more practical to go the rotary or regular planetary route. A number of micrographic users, particularly in the engineering environment, produce the strip-up rolls on the same 35 mm planetary cameras that are used to produce full-frame 35 mm rolls (of engineering drawings, for example). The film in these cases has to be trimmed down to the proper width before being stripped up as a fiche master. Special apparatus is commercially available for both the trimming and stripping operations.

Obviously, the alternative to an in-house operation in which two different microforms are required is to have one of the two, or both, produced by a service bureau.

2. Roll Film Production from Source Documents

As already mentioned, the basic choice here is between planetary and rotary cameras, the comparative advantages and disadvantages of which are summarized in Table C. Note that among the advantages cited for the sophisticated versions of both camera types is the ability to record retrieval coding—"blips," for example—on the film, along with the micro-images. This is a particularly important consideration where rolls, cartridges, or cassettes are to be the system's actual working microform. Even if automated retrieval is not anticipated at the outset, the slight extra cost of providing for it during filming may later prove to have been a very prudent investment.

All that need be added to what the table shows is to reiterate the general rule that it is the nature of the data base, both its physical nature and its content, that will usually determine which of the two basic camera types if best in a given situation.

TABLE C

Generalized Comparison of Planetary and Rotary Cameras; advantages and disadvantages

CAMERA TYPE	ADVANTAGES	DISADVANTAGES
ROTARY (a) Basic	• Even the simplest are largely automated • Easy to operate • Fast (high throughput rate) • Automatic exposure control • Can film both sides of small documents simultanteously • More mobile than planetary	• Limited in the size of original document it can handle • Not cost effective where volume of documents is small • Virtually tied to use of 16mm film • Limited resolution capability
(b) Sophisticated	• All of the above, plus. . . • One camera can film in various formats • Can simultaneously film on two rolls • Can automatically film fanfold computer printout. • Can add "blip" or line coding automatically.	• All of the above, plus... • Comparatively expensive
PLANETARY (a) Basic	• Reduction ratio variable without interchanging heads. • Can film pages of a bound book, or other rigid originals • Adaptable to use of various gauge films • Generally better resolution capability than rotaries • Less expensive than most rotaries (more cost effective at low volumes)	• Strictly manual operation • Relatively slow (low throughput rate) • Generally less mobile than a rotary • Filming format is generally fixed
(b) Sophisticated	• All of the above, plus... • Automatic exposure control • May provide for binary retrieval coding • Step-and-repeat configuration can film fiche directly on 105mm film • May provide for backlighting and projected frame field indication • May be able to film front and rear of documents sequentially and automatically, at high speed.	• Last three of the above, plus... • May be more expensive than a rotary of comparable sophistication.

3. Camera-Processors

Combined camera-processors are available for slightly less than twice the cost of a comparable planetary camera. They are available for practically all microforms, but the EAM aperture card has been the dominant application. Filming is done on chips of exposed silver halide film premounted in aperture cards. The combination is called a *camera card,* and these are automatically stack-fed into the filming position from a lightproof container. The whole device is, in fact, completely automated. All the operator has to do is place the original material on the copyboard and press the right button.

The camera-processor need not, incidentally, be of planetary design. There is at least one flow type camera-processor commercially available. There is also at least one COM device that embodies a processing capability to enable completely automated fiche production.

These devices naturally require a degree of human attention, particularly for maintenance. There are processing chemical reservoirs that require periodic replenishment and cleaning, and the devices are mechanically

127

complex and therefore subject to occasional malfunction or need for adjustment.

Another consideration in selecting camera-processors is their ability to produce output that meets the image permanence requirements for the particular application. Depending on how stringent your requirements are, a particular unit may or may not be able to meet them. Some of these devices may take shortcuts to minimize the complexity of the automated processing mechanism, in which case it is unlikely that they will produce film of "archival" quality.* This should be checked before selecting a particular device for use in a system. At the same time, the costs of the device and of the required special materials have to be weighed against convenience and anticipated volume of usage.

4. COM

As mentioned in an earlier chapter, the Computer Output Microfilmer, variously referred to in the vernacular as a *COM, COM recorder,* or *COM device,* is basically a high-speed, microform-output substitute for either a line printer or plotter, or both, in a data-processing operation. For the purposes of this book, a question that has to be asked, then, is *where does COM fit into the planning of a micrographic system by a records management organization?* There are basically four answers to that question:

(a)   wherever a significant amount of documentation used in an active records-reference environment is presently computer-generated via line printers;

(b)   in many cases where a plotter is presently used to reproduce computer-generated graphics;

(c)   wherever the paper output of either of the above two operations is *subsequently* microfilmed; and

(d)   wherever existing manually-prepared documentation, either paper *or* microform, in an active records-reference environment is, by nature, a *candidate* for computer preparation.

Items (a) and (b) view COM merely as a sophisticated means of substituting microfilm for paper in a data processing environment. Items (c) and (d) on the other hand, indirectly suggest use of COM as a micrographic system shortcut by eliminating one of the traditional steps in the evolution of a microimage. The existing microform referred to in (d) will, like that in (c), have been produced with a microform camera from a paper original.

For a better picture of how COM functions as a shortcut in the kind of situation to which item (d) refers, consider a draftsman producing an engineering drawing by traditional methods. Chances are that an approval print of the finished drawing will be submitted to the engineer, who will either approve it as is, or return it to the drafting department for corrections or changes. In any event, when it is finally released and delivered to the file, it takes its place in the queue at the microform camera. After microfilming, the original drawing must be filed where it will be easy to retrieve when changes have to be made.

The question that COM poses with regard to this situation is, Would it not make more sense for the draftsman or engineer, or both, to shift the energies consumed in the preparation of paper documentation to a system

---

*Archival quality will be discussed in subsection 7, *Quality Control.*

of human-computer interaction that permits the "drawing" to be composed and finalized within the computer's memory? Access to the drawing would then be a relatively simple matter of calling it forth via a COM device, or via a CRT display if it is needed only for quick reference. The COM output would serve as an acceptable master from which duplicates and hard copy can subsequently be produced as needed, and there would be no space-consuming paper tracing to file.* Subsequent changes would be made via the same interactive terminal on which the drawing was originally created.

Interactive graphic terminals for this purpose have, in fact, already been designed and built and are in use in limited numbers in highly specialized engineering environments, usually in research labs, where their comparatively high costs can be justified. But, despite present limitations on the practical use of such systems, their existence indicates a definite future trend in the creation of graphic information. It is a trend that should not be overlooked by system planners whose scope of interests includes graphic communication.

The alphanumeric equivalent of these interactive graphic systems is, of course, *word processing,* which is already in active use in many sectors of the business world. Word-processing systems exist in several forms, in all of which (depending on the application) there is a fairly open choice between paper and COM output.

It is not within the scope of this book to detail what is involved in planning for the use of COM in a micrographic system. An entire book could be devoted to that subject alone. However, it might be useful to identify some of the factors affecting selection of a specific device. Following are the basic considerations:

(a) *ON-LINE/OFF-LINE OPERATION*
Is it capable of both or one or the other? Which one? (Off-line is generally preferred.)

(b) *INPUT*
Is tape drive included? (Some exclude it completely; some offer it as a companion option; some have it built-in.) 7- or 9-track? (The trend is toward 9.) Code sets? (EBCDIC, ASCII, BCD, etc.) Packing density? 556, 800, or 1600 bits per linear inch of tape. (The trend is toward 1600.)

(c) *CHARACTER FONTS*
Number available, styles, sizes.

(d) *CHARACTER DENSITY/CARRIAGE CONTROL*
Characters per line/lines per frame?

(e) *GRAPHICS CAPABILITY*
Is it needed? Does it have it? If it does, what are the line weight and resolution capabilities?

(f) *FORMS OVERLAY*
Optical superimposition of fixed form design, logos, etc. (Most units have it.) Is there a stored program capability for forms selection?

---

*It can be argued, of course, that the space-consuming paper tracing will merely have been supplanted by equally space-consuming magnetic tapes. While this is substantially true, the trend is toward greater and greater compaction of digital data on tape and discs.

(g) *IMAGE ORIENTATION*
"Cine", "comic", fiche formatting.

(h) *FILM TRANSPORT*
Lenses for different reductions included? Control electronics, vacuum hold down, etc. included? Type of Film? What width(s) of film does it accept? Does it accept both perforated and nonperforated film?

(i) *RETRIEVAL CODING*
Does it provide for it? Which codes?

(j) *CONTROLLER (for off-line operation)*
Is one included? What size memory, in kilobits?

(k) *HEADER EXTRACTION*
(For fiche production on 105mm film.) Is it provided for?

(l) *THROUGHPUT SPEED*
Transfer rate of tape data to film, preferably in "pages-per. . ." (unit of time).* Camera speed characteristics? Controller memory cycle? (See above.)

(m) *ERROR DETECTION*
Is it provided for? Are errors corrected, or just reported, or what?

(n) *IMAGE MONITORING*
Is there provision for monitoring what is going onto the film?

(o) *PARTIAL RE-RUN*
Can an isolated output defect be corrected without having to re-run the whole job?

(p) *SERVICE AVAILABILITY*
Where is the nearest service office? How long for a technician to come when called?

Beyond these basic considerations, it will suffice to recognize that COM is normally the province of the data processing environment, and that, if your expertise is confined to the realm of manually-prepared documentation, it is essential that you consult with someone active in data processing before attempting to include COM in a system plan. (Guidelines for negotiating with a commercial service bureau for off-line COM-generation of microforms were given in Chapter 8.)

5. *Separate In-House Processing*

The in-house use of camera-processors has already been discussed. Where COM devices and more conventional microform cameras are used in-house, and it is intended that processing be an in-house operation as well, we need to know something about the available hardware for that purpose.

First, there are basically two types of processors, high-production and office type, of which the latter is the more commonly used in-house. The distinction is probably not as clearly defined as this categorization would make it seem. There is naturally an overlapping area of processors that physically resemble the large production types, but that are sufficiently compact, inexpensive, and easy to install, to qualify as office types. Moreover, in this latter category, there is fairly wide variation in throughput speeds and other capabilities available.

---

*usually given in characters per second (the normal range is about 30,000 to over 100,000). But this may be deceiving.

130

As indicated in Chapter 8 (Table B), a compact, office type processor will cost between $1600 and $6000 to purchase, and will occupy anywhere from one to 14 square feet of floorspace, excluding operating space. A typical unit can process from four to eight feet of film a minute.

Although units are available that do not require special plumbing, this is an aspect of in-house processing that may warrant special attention from the system planner. Assuming that there *is* a plumbing requirement, it could range from a simple hot and cold water mixing valve, and perhaps a minor drain pipe extension, to installation of a whole new, separate waste facility. Local ordinances will usually dictate the specific requirements regarding chemical waste disposal. The American National Standards Institute (ANSI) has recently issued a national standard on the disposal of processing effluents (PH4.37).

Related to waste disposal, and of growing economic importance, is *silver recovery.* One of the components of the effluent from silver film processing is pure silver, the value of which, at the time of writing, is slightly more than $4 per troy ounce. Every effort should be made to recover this material, not only for economic reasons, but also because silver compounds are classed as a toxic pollutant of the environment. Special equipment for the purpose is commercially available from at least two suppliers. It ranges in price from about $500 to over $2000, depending on recovery rate and capacity.

An incidental labor factor that bears brief mention in connection with in-house processing is the frequency with which chemicals have to be replenished and tanks flushed. It is primarily determined by the processor design, and in general, for a given volume of film, the compact, table-top variety will require more attention than the larger machines.

Beyond these considerations, the processor selected naturally has to accept the type and width, or widths, of film to be used in the system, and preferably should permit some flexibility of processing conditions (temperatures, time in developer, etc.) in case it is ever decided to change to a different type of emulsion. A related consideration is the assurance that the processed film will meet all essential end-quality requirements. Of the more familiar items, those that can be adversely affected by improper processing are *archival quality, image background density,* degree of *"fogging"* of the clear portions of the microform, and the amount of *film curl.* Quality control criteria and tests are covered in subsection 7.

One final processing consideration is the desired tonal polarity of the master microforms. Reversal processing to produce nonrevers*ed* camera masters (positive images in a source document system; "negative-appearing" images in a COM system) may require two separate conventional processors. The idea is to only partially process the film initially (partial development; no fixing) then re-expose it to light, and process it the rest of the way. There are also single-unit processors available that are designed specifically for reversal processing. However it is accomplished, it is an added consideration where nonrevers*ed* camera output is required.

6. *Production Duplication*

The other aspect of microform production is duplication, particularly in a situation involving quantity duplication of silver masters for distribution.

Generalized comparison of diazo and vesicular copy films and silver-halide film for microfilm duplication; advantages and disadvantages.

FILM TYPE	ADVANTAGES	DISADVANTAGES
DIAZO	• can be handled in normal room light • simple development (ammonia) • high resolution • good contrast and reproducibility • relatively scratch resistant • cannot be overdeveloped • good shelf life • good image stability (possibly archival) • least expensive	• requires chemical development • underdevelopment can cause subsequent image degradation • development produces fumes (venting required) • slow (slowest of three)
VESICULAR	• can be handled in normal room light • simple heat development (simpler than diazo; no chemicals or fumes) • relatively high resolution • good contrast and print reproducibility • good shelf life • presumably good image stability • faster than diazo	• resolution not quite as good as silver or diazo • images can be degraded by overdevelopment • not recommended for subsequent film-to-film duplication • images less durable than silver or diazo (subject to physical and heat damage) • slower than silver • slightly more expensive than diazo
SILVER	• high resolution • good contrast and reproducibility • choice of reversed or nonreversed polarity • fair shelf life • images not as vulnerable to heat or light damage • archival stability (if properly processed) • fast	• requires darkroom handling • requires multistage chemical processing • images vulnerable to scratching • shorter shelf life than other two (in raw form) • most expensive of the three

NOTE: This table purposely avoids classifying the normal image polarity characteristics of diazo and vesicular films as advantages or disadvantages. However, it is important to recognize that diazo is normally nonreversing (negative from negative) and vesicular is normally reversing (positive from negative).

Besides silver halide film, which can serve as the medium for duplicate as well as master microforms, the two principal film types intended for the purpose are *diazo* and *vesicular.* The latter are strictly copy films (not for camera use), and each has its own exclusive set of characteristics. Table D gives some comparisons that will help in selecting the type of film for use as the production duplication medium in a system.

Beyond selection of film type, a decision has to be made as to whether the work will be done outside by a service bureau or in-house, and, if the latter, what type of duplication hardware will be required to meet the needs of the system. Among the principal considerations in either case are anticipated production volumes and costs, both of which have already been covered elsewhere in this book (duplication volumes in this chapter, and costs in Chapter 8). One other important consideration that relates strictly to in-house diazo duplication is the safety aspect of the use of ammonia as the diazo developer. It is advisable that local safety ordinances and Federal safety recommendations be checked beforehand for required equipment approvals, venting provisions, storage routines, etc.

In fiche and card systems, duplication and distribution can be linked together via special high production duplicators that can be programmed to produce a given quantity of copies from each master and to sort them automatically into separate stacks. In at least one such commercially available fiche machine, the number of duplicates is controlled by the sensing of an optical bar code recorded on the header of the master fiche.

Another way in which fiche distribution can be at least semi-automated is by use of an automatic merger/inserter, a common mail-handling device, specially modified to handle fiche without risk of damage to the images. Like the automated duplicator just described, this device can intermix the duplicated fiche sheets in accordance with a predetermined optical code.

7. Quality Control

Quality inspection of microform production is vital to the smooth functioning and effectiveness of a micrographic system. Imagine discovering, too late, that hundreds of thousands of microimages of documents that have since been destroyed have poor archival permanence*, because, for example, the hypo was not thoroughly removed in processing and, consequently, the images are fading at a rate that will render them useless before the required retention period is up. A simple spot check of the processor output would have detected the condition and enabled its correction with a minimum of lost time and materials.

That is one possibility. Of more immediate concern, however, are the facts that excessively warped fiche, for example, may cause malfunctioning of an automated retrieval system; that low resolution of images will adversely affect readability; and that low contrast may adversely affect subsequent reproduction.

All such disastrous possibilities can be effectively headed off by providing for relatively simple and inexpensive inspection facilities in the system design. Chapter 8 (Table N) provides a hint of the required investment: a total of about $1200 for the essentials, namely a *densitometer, microscope, light box* and *rewinds.* Chemicals and apparatus to test for residual thiosulfate (hypo, or fixer), the principal cause of long-term silver image destruction, will increase the total cost by anywhere from a few dollars to a few hundred dollars, depending on the type of test and the degree of accuracy desired. Some managers of micrographic systems find it more practical to have this test performed by a local microfilm service bureau.

For the user who intends to perform residual hypo tests on-premises, a few words are needed on the various methods and their limitations. One of the older standard methods is the mercuric-chloride, or *Ross-Crabtree* test, which, despite certain critical requirements, is basically a subjective test offering results that are, at best, only moderately reliable. It has been generally replaced by two newer methods—the *methylene blue* and *silver densitometric* tests.

The methylene blue test is more precise than the Ross-Crabtree, but also more complex and costly. Its major drawbacks are that it requires a spectrophotometer—a comparatively costly instrument—as a measuring de-

---

*Archival *permanence* is also known variously as archival *quality* and archival *stability.*

Typical resolution, density, and film bow criteria for quality inspection of original silver film.

RESOLUTION (minimum, as read on film, in terms of smallest NBS pattern resolved)		
CLASS OF MATERIAL (and reduction)	CAMERA TYPE	
	ROTARY	PLANETARY
Documents (24X)	2.8	4.5
Eng'g Dwgs		
(16X)	-	7.1
(24X)	-	5.0
(30X)	-	4.5

TRANSMISSION DENSITY (In density units, as measured with a properly calibrated visual diffuse transmission densitometer)	
Background, Source Document Images—	
General, on Fiche or 16 mm:	0.90 - 1.30
Eng's Dwgs on 35mm:	1.00 - 1.20
Newspaper Pages on 35 mm:	0.90 - 1.40
Background, COM:	min. 1.20
Linework (Equiv.), COM:	approx. 0.35

MAX. BOW (within film width)	
35 mm, for aperture card mounting:	1/16 inch
Fiche:	1/4 inch

vice, and use of some potentially hazardous chemicals. The silver densitometric method provides generally adequate accuracy and is relatively simple and inexpensive. It requires three chemical "dips" to produce and fix a stain on a portion of a processed film specimen. The stained and unstained portions of the specimen are then measured and compared on an ordinary transmission densitometer equipped with a special filter. Although a good densitometer is a quite expensive piece of test apparatus, it is an item that any properly equipped inspection facility will already include.

As noted in Appendix C, details of these two newer methods are covered in ANSI Standard PH4.8-1971. In addition, ANSI Standards PH1.28-1973 and PH1.41-1973 are the basis for the prescribed limit of 0.7 micrograms of residual thiosulfate ions per square centimeter of film.

Other quality tests, such as those for visual defects, image reduction, resolution, and density, are covered quite thoroughly in NMA Recommended Practice MS104-1972, "Inspection and Quality Control of First Generation Silver Halide Microfilm". In summary, however, the data in Table E will serve as guidelines in the inspection of original silver film for resolution, density, and bow. Additional published standards on production quality criteria will be found listed in Appendix C under the heading INSPECTION, TESTING, MEASURING.

So much for silver film. Equally important is production quality control of duplicate microforms. Unfortunately, there is a relative scarcity of published standards in this area, the principal reason being that there are various technical problems involved in attempting to set uniform quality standards for copy film images. For example, the dark areas of a diazo image, unlike those of a silver image, are spectrally selective, and a given visual density measurement will therefore not apply equally to the film's viewing and printing characteristics. Because of this, density criteria for diazo duplicates are generally based on *linework density*, rather than background, as in the case of silver film.

As a production quality control, actual readings of diazo "line" density are made on duplicates of a silver test frame containing images of 25 and 50 percent reflectance test patches, and on which the latter produced a visual diffuse reading of about 1.10 density units. The currently accepted criteria for diazo density is a reading of about 0.35 density units for the *25 percent* patch (representing line density) on a first generation duplicate of the silver test frame. Once the duplicator has been "fine-tuned" to produce this result, an occasional visual inspection of the output will generally suffice.

Bear in mind that the above criteria pertain strictly to *diazo* duplication. As of this writing, there is no comparable density check method for vesicular images. Probably the most effective production quality control technique for vesicular is to spot check the duplicator output on a conventional reader-printer.

As pointed out in Chapter 7, the accepted norm for resolution of duplicate images is a degradation of no more than one NBS pattern from that of the master image (or per subsequent duplication generation). This criterion applies in general to vesicular as well as diazo images, although it should be somewhat easier to meet with diazo.

Archival stability, which has been discussed with regard to original silver film, is also a factor in production duplication. There is no chemical test as there is for silver, and there is, in fact, no sure way of estimating the lasting qualities of duplicate microimages on diazo or vesicular film. However, an experienced operator will usually be able to spot an underdeveloped duplicate, and, by making the necessary developer corrections, to minimize the possibility of subsequent image destruction by exposure to intense light, as in a reader.

Incomplete development of vesicular film (insufficient heat) is usually detectable as a color change in the exposed areas. The nature of the change will depend on the particular brand and type of vesicular film used, and its detection must therefore be a matter of experience on the operator's part.

With diazo film, a test procedure is usually necessary to verify a suspected underdevelopment condition. One test is simply to measure the density of a dark portion of an output specimen, watching for a gradually decreasing reading while the densitometer "probe" is held in the operating position. Another is to measure the density of a given spot on a developed specimen, put it through the developer again, and measure the same spot for a noticeable change in density. A third test is to fully process the duplicate of a specific image, then expose a different image on top of the first one, reprocess, and check visually for a superimposed "ghost" of the second image on the first.

One final quality control consideration applies to master and copy film alike. Mention has been made of film *bow*, a term normally applying to curvature within the *width* of the film with respect to its existence in roll form. Equally important in production quality control is film *curl*—curvature along the film's *length*. Technically, there should be no curl in roll film that is being mounted in aperture cards. The natural curl of the film can usually be removed by reverse winding it prior to mounting. Curl in fiche is equally undesirable, particularly in automated retrieval situations. One way to prevent it is through use of thicker film. In general, the thinner the film, the more prone is to curl.

III. File Design Considerations

The file is the nucleus of a micrographic system. Viewed as a system component in its own right, it is really a kind of abstraction that can assume many forms. It can range, for example, from a single fiche sheet to an entire room of hardware, possibly including a variety of separate mechanical devices. It can even be broken up and scattered over a wide geographic area, and it can be accessed electronically if that is feasible.

For the purposes of this discussion, we will regard the file as a centralized entity consisting of multiple components and having multiple functions, the combined objective of which is to provide the user with information resources in the form, *and time frame,* in which they are needed. Following is a list of the basic components, which, collectively, will be regarded as constituting the file:

1. Filing hardware
2. Retrieval hardware
3. Reference readers and/or reader printers *(Note:* 1, 2, and 3 may be combined as a single component.)
4. Demand duplicators
5. Demand printers
    (Note: 4 and 5 may be regarded as alternatives, or may both be optional.)
6. Keypunch reproducer/interpreters (EAM aperture card systems only; optional for use in connection with demand duplication.)
7. (optional) EDP support for automated retrieval
8. (optional) Communication facilities for remote accessing.

Components such as high-volume duplicators, printers and EAM card-handling equipment, strip-up or jacket-filling apparatus, film-to-card mounters, etc., will be regarded as *production* components, along with cameras, COMs, processors, and inspection equipment. While these components will often be found in the general vicinity of the file, and may even be under the same organizational umbrella, they will be regarded as technically separate from the file. Similarly, the microform file tray and the reader or reader-printer at a user's work location will not be considered part of the file, *per se,* although technically they are appendages of it.

Following are the basic considerations affecting file design:
1. Physical size of the data base.
2. Anticipated growth.
3. Anticipated accessing activity.
4. Anticipated update activity (revison & purging)
5. Retention durations.

6. Convenience of access.
7. Security considerations.
8. Output formats

Now let's briefly examine each of these to see how they interrelate in the evolution of a physical file configuration.

1. *Physical Size of the Data Base*

Here we are looking at the data base in microform, following conversion from paper or magnetic tape. The space it occupies will depend essentially on the microform selected and the reduction ratio (the *effective* ratio in the case of COM-produced microimages). Table D in Chapter 8 gives representative physical requirements for a sampling of data base sizes and for each of five microforms using typical image formats. If there are any simple rules governing the minimizing of file size, they are that (a) fiche theoretically makes the most efficient use of space, although the physical design of the available filing hardware may give roll film a slight edge; and (b) the greater the reduction ratio (or *effective* ratio), the smaller the physical file. The risk in being too strongly influenced by this latter rule is that attempts to reduce the physical size of the file by going to higher image reductions may impose high production costs and may adversely affect legibility of the enlarged microimages. It may also have an adverse effect on convenience of access. More will be said on this later.

2. *Anticipated Growth*

The rate of file growth will depend on several factors, among which are:
(a) the flow rate of incoming records that must be retained,
(b) the retention periods for the various classes of documents involved,
(c) the efficiency with which the file is kept purged.

In any event, reasonable allowances for growth have to be included in the system plan, particularly with regard to hardware needs and space allocation. Depending on its rate, it may also have a bearing on projected labor needs.

A useful design feature to keep in mind in this regard is *modularity,* particularly if your system will embody automated retrieval in some form. In selecting hardware for the purpose, it might be wise to consider systems that permit modular expansion of the central store that is accessible from a given retrieval terminal.

A good guideline to follow in estimating file growth is the generally accepted statistic that the rate of growth of support documentation is approximately double the rate of growth of the business it supports.

3. *Anticipated Accessing Activity*

The rate at which the file is accessed will affect its design to the extent that it is arranged to facilitate the task. Following are some examples of how accessing activity can be facilitated in a manual filing situation:
a. *File integrity*—Provision for strict confinement of the masters to the file area so that they are sure to be available when needed; provision for rapid return of each master to its proper place in the file as soon as a request has been served (These are, of course, procedural matters);

137

b.   *File organization*—Arrangement of the file in a systematic and orderly manner, consistent with its content;

c.   *Location aids*—Use of color tabs; file separators; color headers on fiche; clear and concise labeling of reels, cartridges, and file drawers or trays; color-coding of EAM image cards; etc.

d.   *Redundancy*—provision of two or more complete master files to permit simultaneous access to the same document by two or more persons.

In a semiautomated system, items (a) and (b), *integrity* and *organization,* may still apply. But, in a fully automated system, these items will be automatically ensured. Item (c), *location aids,* can be ignored for automated systems, in general. The need for item (d), *redundancy,* on the other hand, may apply as well to automated as to manual files. Depending on the level of accessing activity and the amount of redundancy it may demand, a computer-controlled automated retrieval system may be worth considering. As long as the system can be kept fairly busy, there are potential economies in the use of a single, central processing unit (CPU) to control multiple users stations.

4.   Anticipated Update Activity

As in the case of accessing activity, the rate at which the file will have to be revised and purged will affect its design to the extent that it is arranged to facilitate the task. With the exception of redundancy, the same considerations (see above) will generally apply. There is, however, one further consideration with regard to automated retrieval systems, and that is the ability to *randomly* file new input. Several commercial systems offer this capability, and it is one that can save considerable time, not only in entering new material into the file, but, in the case of some semi-automated systems, in returning material that has been temporarily removed to meet a reference request.

5.   Retention Durations

The retention consideration has already been alluded to in connection with space and hardware needs. Besides the fairly obvious fact that the retention periods for the filed microforms have to be considered in estimating these needs, there is also the possibility that allowances will have to be made for simultaneous retention of the *original paper file* as well.

Company policy may be the sole determinant of retention periods in some cases, but federal, state, and local laws may also be involved. It is advisable that the retention question be thoroughly examined before a physical file plan is finalized.

Even if paper and inactive microform files do have to be retained for relatively lengthy periods, they can at least be exiled to otherwise wasted (and therefore relatively inexpensive) storage space. However, they should have essentially the same protection against the elements and against possible disaster that the active file has.

6.   Convenience of Access

This consideration, like retention durations, has already been adequately covered. *Redundancy,* for example, has been mentioned as one possible way to ensure simultaneous access to the same material by two or more persons in a busy file. The alternative is *queuing delays,* which, of course, should be minimized to ensure an efficient file operation.

Other ways of ensuring accessing convenience in a comparatively large and busy file operation, in addition to redundancy, automated retrieval, and the use of location aids, are:

(a) applying height restrictions on filing hardware so that drawers, trays, etc. are neither too high nor too close to the floor. Space may have to be sacrificed for convenience; more on this in the discussion of space requirements later in this chapter;

(b) using "tub" or mechanized rotary files;

(c) organizing the file so that separate items likely to require simultaneous access are filed separately, or so that high demand items will be located in the most convenient place.

Selection of the microform will obviously have a bearing on the extent to which this last approach (item c) can be applied. *Partial redundancy* might even be considered, i.e., provision of duplicates of only those items likely to have the highest accessing activity.

7. *Security Considerations*

The word *security,* as applied to a file operation, has three meanings, any one, or any combination, of which may apply in a given situation. They are:

(a) physical security of the file against loss or misplacement of the filed masters;

(b) securing of the file's information content on a "need-to-know" basis;

(c) protection of the physical file masters against excessive heat, moisture, etc., and disaster, such as fire or flooding.

The first of these has already been covered in discussions of file integrity, and all that need be added at this point is a reminder that fully automated retrieval is about the only absolute insurance against loss or misplacement of file masters.

The second item, securing the file's information content on a "need-to-know" basis, can usually be handled as a simple procedural matter in a manual file operation. At the very least, the user might be required, for example, to display employee identification. However, where retrieval is automated, "need-to-know" access may not be quite so easy to implement. This is particularly true of a *semi*-automated configuration, in which, for example, the user directly selects a cartridge for manual insertion in a retrieval/display unit. The simplest way, of course, would be a "guard-at-the-door" arrangement in which no one is admitted to the file area without showing proper identification. Another possibility would be the use of a novel alerting system that has been adopted by some libraries to prevent book thefts—a small piece of special magnetic tape is attached to each book or other hand-transportable item, and a special detection device is installed at the library exit. Unless the item has been properly checked out, an alarm is set off if its possessor attempts to leave the premises with it. In a micrographic system having rolls as the microform, the tape could perhaps be placed on the film, at the end closest to the reel hub, where it would activate the alarm but not be visible to the user.

In a fully automated system where retrieval codes have to be manually keyed-in, provision might be made for the keying-in of an access code to initially "unlock" the unit. In its simplest form, this could be a single, fixed code, revealed only to those individuals entitled to use the file. However, the more secure approach would be to program the system to recognize any of several individually assigned codes identifying users. This alternative would, of course, be easiest to apply in a computer-aided retrieval system.

As for protection of the file masters against environmental damage, this is simply a matter of prudent choice of the file site and observance of established environmental control, and fire and flood prevention practices.

8. *Output Formats*

The nature of the file and the user environment should determine the necessary output format(s). Of the three choices—reader screen images, duplicate microforms, and hard copy—any one or a combination may be required in a given situation. Table F illustrates typical needs for a sampling of user environments. Let's take a moment to analyze the information contained in the table.

TABLE F

Typical file output requirements for a sampling of user environments.

APPLICATION— END USER	OUTPUT FORMAT		
	VIEW MASTER IN READER AT FILE	EXPENDABLE DUPLICATE MICROFORMS	HARD COPY PRODUCED FROM FILE MASTER
AIRLINE RESERVATIONS— SERVICE CLERK	x		
ENG. DWGS— (a) PLANNING ENGRS. (b) DESIGN ENGRS.	x x	x x	x
PROCUREMENT— BIDDER		x	
TECH. REPORTS LIBRARY— ENGINEER		x	x
CATALOG LIBRARY— GENERAL USER	x		x
NEWSPAPER PAGE REPRINT SERVICE— GEN'L PUBLIC			x

In the airline reservations application, it is the airline schedules that are on microform, and these need only be called up on a viewing screen for quick reference in connection with telephone inquiries. However, the user of engineering drawings will generally use the reader at the file only to determine the drawing sheets required, and then will request duplicates or prints to use at his or her own desk. For the planning engineer, duplication for reader reference will usually suffice, but the design engineer may additionally require hard copy on which to make engineering changes.

The prospective bidder in the procurement application receives what is generally known as a "bid package," literally a package of microforms conveying technical information on components or equipment on which formal bids are being sought from a number of vendors. The duplicate microforms are distributed in lieu of paper and therefore reduce bulk and save distribution and handling costs.

The technical reports library in our example fulfills user requests with a choice of duplicate microform (usually fiche) or a paper copy of the original report. The catalog library, on the other hand, which is accessed directly by the user on a conventional reader-printer, is basically a quick reference system in which the screen image will probably suffice in most cases. The print option satisfies the occasional need for hard copy of specific catalog pages.

The newspaper page reprint service is included in the Table merely as an example of a system in which the end user would expect hard copy exclusively. The microform will normally be 35mm reels and the hard copy is produced on an enlarger-printer.

Once the output formats of the file have been decided upon, the next decision involves the *quantities* of reproduction hardware required to satisfy anticipated levels of accessing activity. For duplicators and hard copy printers, there are relatively fixed throughput speeds to gauge by. For example, a given duplicator might take 15 seconds to produce each finished fiche or EAM card duplicate on a demand basis. The range is roughly 6 to 30 seconds, and it is about the same for hard copy printers. Thus, depending on volume, a given file operation will need X number of separate units of a given speed to meet the demand for duplicates or prints.

The number of readers or reader-printers required at the file is another matter. It is difficult to estimate how long the typical user is likely to study a reader screen image in a given situation. No doubt studies have been made along these lines, but there are really too many variables for any such study to be universally applicable. Probably the best approach in most cases is to make an intuitive guess at the number of readers or reader-printers that might be required at the outset, and allow space and funds for additional units as needed. This, incidentally, does not include readers and reader-printers for use away from the file—at the user's desk, for example. This need will be discussed in section IV.

Quality, as well as quantity, can affect file design to the extent that, as in a production situation, some minimal provision must be made for quality control of duplicator output. For demand duplication at the file, a simple visual inspection (holding the fiche or card to a light and checking subjectively for contrast, image alignment, blemishes, etc.) may suffice. But, for better assurance of user satisfaction, a quick examination of each duplicate microform in a reader is advisable.

IV   User Hardware

In the planning of micrographic systems that will include reading, reproducing and satellite filing hardware separate from the central file, some thought must naturally be given to the criteria for selection of such equipment. There are two basic configurations to consider in this regard:
(a)   a reader or reader-printer facility central to a multiperson office or office area;
(b)   individual, desk-top readers or reader-printers.
Either configuration might include limited microform filing facilities.

Let's briefly examine the components.

1. *Readers*

Selection of a desk-top reader involves a three-way trade-off of design parameters. First, we will want the unit to be as compact as possible. But compactness affects screen size as well as the desk area occupied. So, secondly, a reasonable compromise must be struck between overall compactness and screen size. Screen size, in turn, to the extent that it influences the choice of magnification, may affect readability, or the degree of comfort with which we can view the screen image. Thirdly, therefore, we will not, in the name of compactness, want to reduce magnification beyond the point where we begin to risk eye strain.

This last parameter—magnification, or "blowback"—may be the logical starting point in selecting a desk-top reader, and the first consideration in this regard is *character size.* Using actual source documents as a point of reference, there are two well established guidelines that can be followed. One is that a 50 percent, or half-size, enlargement from the microimage has proved to be a tolerable minimum for engineering drawings using standard 1/8-inch characters; and the other is that approximately a 2/3 enlargement has proved generally adequate for typewriter and typical text fonts (e.g., 24X reduction; 15X blowback). From these criteria, if follows that a 1:1 reduction/enlargement ratio will probably be required for small characters such as those found in newspaper legal notices and telephone directories.

The logical next question is, will the user be able to tolerate a magnification/screen size relationship that results in less than a full page image on the screen at one time? If the answer is yes, then a more compact desk-top unit is possible. This is a particularly important question with regard to engineering drawings and other larger-than-letter-size documents, for which a *scanning type* reader may be a virtual necessity in a typical desk-top situation.

With an appropriate compromise having been struck between magnification and screen size, the overall size of the reader will pretty much take care of itself. Bear in mind, though, that there is no rigid rule that says a reader must have a built-in screen. Two alternatives are *hand-viewing* and *projection.*

The hand-held viewers for microforms are not much different from those for viewing slides. (See Fig. 9.1.) The microform is inserted in a slot and the viewer lens is placed to the eye. Like some inexpensive slide viewers, it may have to be "aimed" at an existing light source for illumination. But there are also models available with built-in illumination. Besides its compactness, the hand viewer offers maximum viewing privacy. It is not recommended, however, for prolonged or frequent viewing, nor is it applicable to some of the higher reduction microforms.

Projection is one way around the need to compromise on magnification and screen size in order to minimize the desk space a reader occupies. A projection type (screenless) reader makes use of any convenient reflective surface, a blank wall, for example, as its screen. (See Fig. 9.2.) Such units are available for practically all standard microforms and at prices roughly comparable to those of conventional desk-top readers. For the individual user, a possible disadvantage of projection is that it does not offer quite the privacy of a more conventional reader.

Fig. 9.1. A selection of hand-held viewers for microforms. Among the various features offered are built-in illumination, ability to view micro-opaques as well as transparent microforms, and interchangeability of lenses. The units save space and provide complete viewing privacy. They range in price from approximately $5 to $80.

Fig. 9.2. Microform projectors require little desk space and can utilize any good reflecting surface as the viewing screen.

144

Selecting a reader for shared use within an office area should be a somewhat easier task because the same space restrictions need not necessarily apply. Chances are the reader will have its own stand or table.

While size is an important factor in the selection of a desk-top reader, there are several other factors to consider in selecting microform readers in general. Among them are:

(a) *Media*—
Does it accept the type or types of microform from which the user will normally be accessing information? A multi-media unit may warrant consideration, particularly for a shared use situation.

(b) *Illumination*—
Is it adequate? Is it fairly consistent over the entire screen?

(c) *Focus*—
Is it sufficiently sharp and reasonably consistent over the entire screen? Can it be finely adjusted?

(d) *Microform Carriage*—
Is it conveniently located? Can the microform be easily inserted?

(e) *Controls*—
Are the necessary ones provided and are they conveniently placed? Do they respond positively to manipulation without being difficult to work?

(f) *Screen Angle*—
Is it right for comfortable viewing?

(g) *Heat and Noise*—
Does the temperature of any external parts of the reader become uncomfortably high after prolonged use? Is there excessive noise from a cooling fan, advance mechanism, etc.?

A representative sampling of commercially available microform readers is depicted in Figure 1.12 of Chapter 1.

2. *Reader-Printers*

Apart from some occasional cleaning of glass and perhaps some minor lubrication of moving parts, microform readers usually require relatively little routine maintenance. This is particularly true of fiche and card readers, which do not require film advance mechanisms. The maintenance situation is somewhat less favorable for reader-printers, which, of necessity, contain additional mechanisms to divert the optical path and to feed the print paper. Moreover, some reader-printers also require use of chemical developers, which results in additional maintenance tasks. (See Chapter 7.)

The matter of maintenance makes it generally impractical to consider widespread placement of reader-printers on user's desks. There is somewhat more margin for practicality in the shared use of a single reader-printer within an office area. But, even here, the need for routine maintenance must not be overlooked. Lax or improper maintenance of a reader-printer using chemical developers can result in an unreliable machine and costly repairs. Thus, where reader-printers are absolutely required at work locations away from the central file, but where there is some question as to whether continuous maintenance can be economically provided, machines using dry printing processes should be considered.

Whatever has already been said about factors to consider in making a selection of readers applies also to reader-printers. In addition, the following considerations are associated strictly with the print function:

(a) *Chemical characteristics (wet process)—*
Are developing chemicals subject to spoilage? Corrosive? Safely confined within the machine?

(b) *Physical characteristics of prints—*
Do prints emerge dry from the machine? Are they naturally tacky to the touch? Do they tend to wrinkle or curl? Can they be marked?

(c) *Print image characteristics—*
Is resolution consistent with that of the screen image? Is focus sufficiently sharp over the entire print area? Is the black-white polarity what the user prefers? Do the images have sufficient contrast, consistent with that of the microimage?

(d) *Availability of consumables—*
Is the continued availability of special paper and developing chemicals assured?

Figure 1.13 in Chapter 1 shows a typical selection of reader-printers, and Chapter 7 contains a discussion of the comparative advantages of various print processes used in currently available units.

3. *User files*

Filing hardware associated with a shared reader or reader-printer station central to a work area can be essentially the same as that used in a central file (a cabinet of drawers, for example). For the individual user, however, something more compact will usually suffice. A wide variety of trays, boxes, book type files, etc., is commercially available for the purpose. Figure 9-3 depicts a representative selection.

V. *General Design Considerations*

So far, this chapter has dwelt mainly on the physical and mechanical aspects of a micrographic system. Certainly not to be deemphasized are the broader, less tangible considerations, such as overall cost, the total labor and space requirements of the system, environmental factors (air conditioning, safety, etc.), and quality control.

The subject of system cost was covered in Chapter 8 and need not be further discussed here except for the perhaps obvious reminder that a proposal for a micrographic system, like that for practically any new or different way of achieving some end, will usually have to be backed by a plausible case for anticipated savings. (More on this in the next chapter.)

1. *Labor Requirements*

Labor requirements will depend, of course, on the nature, size, and level of activity of the system. It is naturally to be hoped that the micrographic system will require less total labor than the system it replaces, or less than some other alternative route might have required. But it is recognized that this may not always be the case.

A well-planned system will apportion the required labor as efficiently as possible. For example, in the 15 or 20 minutes that it may take for a roll of film to process (assuming in-house processing), the processor operator could be performing some additional task, such as keypunching tab cards in connection with preparation of a look-up index or aperture cards, if it is

Fig. 9.3. A selection of microform filing devices for private use away from the central file.

that kind of system. Similarly, during periods of low user service activity, a service clerk could remain busy in the task of updating and purging the file.

The other aspect of labor requirement is the level of skill. Obviously, the greater the skill required, the higher the salary that must be paid. Generally speaking, the skill needed to operate and maintain a manual micrographic system should be no greater than that required for a manual paper file. Experience has shown that operation of conventional microreproduction equipment of the type used within a file environment can be learned quite readily by relatively nonskilled personnel. Although a camera, processor, automated retrieval device, and perhaps some types of keypunch equipment may take longer to learn to operate than a duplicator or hard copy printer, the required skills are not necessarily any greater.

The tasks for which a higher level of skill may be necessary are those associated with data processing and human-computer interaction. Operation of a COM recorder, for example, may require greater skill than operation of a planetary camera or film processor. Depending on the nature of the system, and who does what, computer-aided retrieval may require some special skills or learning abilities on the part of personnel directly associated with the micrographic system.

In seeking people for training in some of the special skills required, don't overlook the handicapped. Various institutions have launched programs in which all sorts of handicapped individuals, some of them homebound, have been successfully trained to perform a variety of micrographics jobs. Some informative articles on the subject are included among the Additional Reading references at the end of this chapter.

2. *Space Requirements*

The main thing to recognize regarding space is that there are several factors that will separately influence the total space requirement for implementation of a micrographic system. The fundamental ones are:
 (a) the present size (and nature) of the data base;
 (b) the anticipated rate of growth;
 (c) retention requirements;
 (d) the type(s) of microform;
 (e) the decision as to whether filming, processing, and duplicating will be done in-house or outside;
 (f) the anticipated levels of accessing and updating activities;
 (g) the file output requirements.

The specific space requirements for hardware items constituting the physical file and production facilities will naturally be influenced by all of these fundamental factors.

One very important additional consideration regarding hardware space requirements is that, besides the actual physical dimensions of the equipment, allowance will generally have to be made for one or more of the following:
 (a) operating or accessing space;
 (b) maintenance space;
 (c) venting space.

For the first of these, Figure 9-4 will serve as a good general guideline. Al-

148

Fig. 9.4. General space requirements for operation and maintenance of micrographic equipment. In addition to the dimensions shown, extra space may also have to be allowed for venting (of heat or fumes) and for the opening of access doors or drawers.

though a seated person is depicted in the figure, the dimensions shown will generally apply as well to a stand-up situation. In addition to the data shown, the recommended maximum vertical reach area for a seated operator is from about 15 inches above the floor to about 60 inches. For a standing operator, the recommended area is from about 30 inches to about 80 inches above the floor.

These same dimensions will apply in general to maintenance space as well, except that appropriate allowances have to be made for the opening of doors, for example. Whether the operating and maintenance space are one and the same or must be separately provided will depend on the design of the equipment. As for venting space, equipment that does not have to dissipate heat or fumes will not require it. Where it *is* required, the equipment supplier's recommendations should be followed.

149

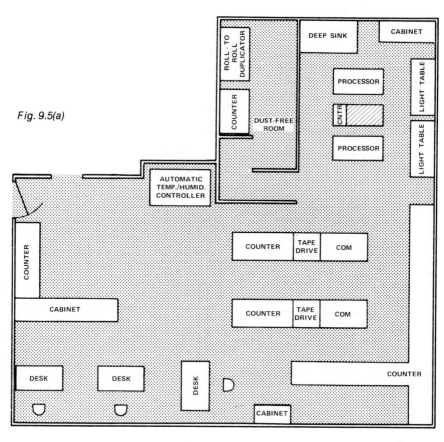

Fig. 9.5(a)

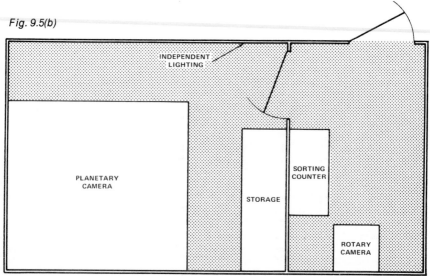

Fig. 9.5(b)

150

Fig. 9.5(c)

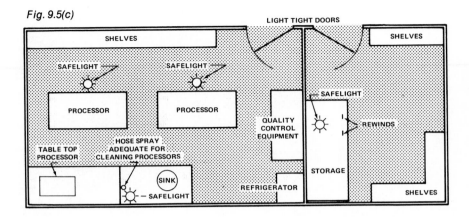

Fig. 9.5. Representative layouts for micrographic production facilities: (a, left) a typical COM installation, (b, left) a source document filming facility, (c, above) a processing and film handling area, and (d, below) a duplication quality control and microform preparation facility.

Fig. 9.5(d)

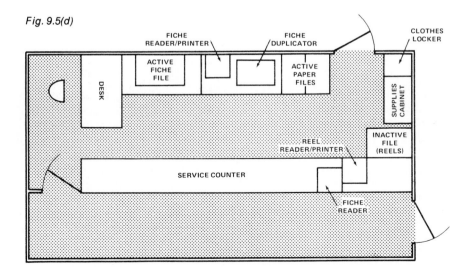

151

Fig. 9.6(a)

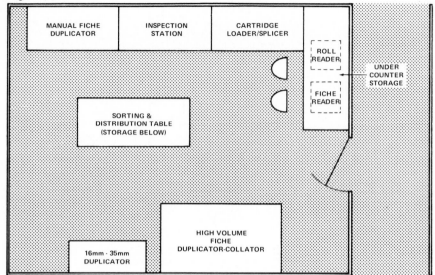

Figures 9-5 and 9-6 show some representative floor plans for micrographic production facilities and service files. Besides the space occupied by furniture and equipment, and the related allowances for accessing, maintenance and venting, about the only other specific dimensional requirements that are essential to practical space planning are those affecting personnel mobility. The usual minimum criteria for aisle widths are 2-1/2 feet for single individual passage and four feet where two individuals have to be able to pass by one another. Where one side of an aisle contains file cabinets, an additional two feet (minimum) should be added to allow for the opening of drawers.

3. Environmental Factors

In this category, we will conveniently lump together such factors as temperature and humidity, personnel safety, and electrical and plumbing requirements. Depending on the climate in which the micrographic system (particularly the central file) exists, temperature and humidity control may or may not be required. In hot and humid environments, conventional air conditioning is recommended, primarily for the preservation of the filed microform masters.

For personnel safety, OSHA requirements should be followed especially with regard to electrical safety and to the storage and use of film processing chemicals (including ammonia, where diazo copy film is used).

Electrical power and plumbing requirements will, of course, depend on the particular equipment to be used in the system. But, in any event, an advance estimate of the need is important at least from the standpoint of knowing whether special utility installations must be included in the projected cost of implementing the system.

VI. Preparing a Flowchart

To aid in planning a system graphically on paper, NMA has established a standard set of flowchart symbols and has made them available in

Fig. 9.6(b)

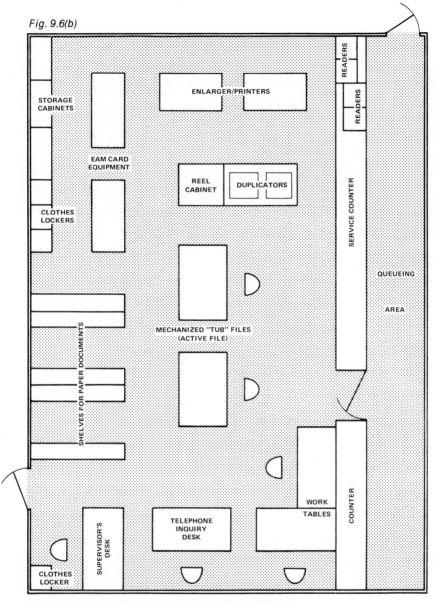

Fig. 9.6. Two possible central service file layouts: (a, left) a small, low volume file containing an active physical data base of some 250,000 document pages on microfiche, backed up by a small inactive and paper file; and (b, above) a medium-to-large, relatively high volume file containing a million or more active document pages on a mix of fiche and aperture cards. In both layouts, liberal accommodation has been made for growth, and, in the larger of the two, a degree of redundancy has also been allowed for.

Template form. Figure 9-7 shows the various symbols and briefly explains the significance of each. Details on use of the symbols in preparation of a micrographics system flowchart are contained in the published NMA standard, MS4-1972 (also available from the American National Standards Institute as ANSI Standard PH5.17-1973). This standard is, in most respects, compatible with the earlier ANSI X 3.5 flowchart standard for general information processing. The principal distinction is the inclusion in MS4 of a set of four symbols specifically relating to micrographics (the first four in figure 9-7).

 ⬜	**ALL MICROFORMS** Represents any microform used in a micrographic systems flow.
 ⊏⊐	**MICROFORM RECORDING** Represents the recording function of transferring information to an original microform master.
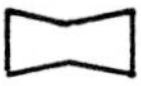 ⊲⊳	**DEVELOPING** Represents the developing process for making information or a medium permanent and/or readable by man or machine.
 ∞	**DUPLICATING** Represents the making of a single or multiple copies of a document or microform, usually with the aid of a master or intermediate.
 ⊏	**STORAGE/RETRIEVAL — ON-LINE** Represents an input/output operation utilizing any type of on-line storage.
▽	**STORAGE/RETRIEVAL — OFF-LINE** Represents the storing of information off-line, regardless of the medium on which the information is recorded.
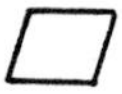 ▱	**INPUT/OUTPUT** Making information available for processing (input) or the recording of processed information (output). The abbreviation of input/output in I/0.
 ⬭	**DOCUMENT** A medium for conveying information usually in paper form.
⬜	**PREDEFINED PROCESS** A process consisting of one or more operations that are specified elsewhere.
▭	**PROCESSING** Any operation on data where the operation is the execution of a defined action.
 ◇	**DECISION** A determination of direction to follow when given a number of alternative paths.
 ⊏	**MANUAL INPUT** The entry of data into a computer or system by direct manual manipulation of a device.
⬜	**AUXILIARY OPERATION** An off-line operation performed on equipment not under direct control of the central processing unit.
∨ > ∧ <	**INFORMATION FLOW** Indicates the direction in which information is transmitted from one location to another. Used most often with the Communication Link symbol.

Fig. 9.7. (above and right) Standard flowchart symbols for micrographic system planning.

154

COMMUNICATION LINK The automatic transmission of information from one location to another.	
○	CONNECTOR A means of representing on a flowchart the junction of two lines of flow or a break in a single line of flow.
	PUNCHED CARD A card that is punched with a combination of holes to represent letters, digits, or special characters.
	MANUAL OPERATION Offline process using human techniques and associated speeds.
	TERMINAL A point in a system or communication network at which data can enter or leave, e.g. start, stop, delay, or interrupt.
	MAGNETIC TAPE Representation of a medium on wihch data is recorded.
	DISPLAY A device on which visual representation of data is shown, e.g. online indicators, video devices, console printers, and plotters.

Besides standardizing a set of symbols, MS4 provides basic guidelines for annotation within a symbol. For example, within the *microform* symbol, standard annotations will include *size* (or width) of film, *generation* (1st, 2nd, 3rd, etc.), image *polarity* (negative or positive), *medium* (silver, diazo, vesicular), and *form* (roll, fiche, aperture card, etc.)

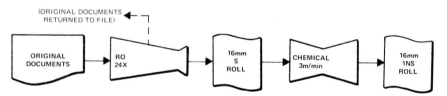

Fig. 9.8. Use of flowchart symbols to depict a basic micrographic system. The original documents are filmed on a 16mm rotary camera, and the processed camera negatives are retained in roll form.

Figure 9-8 shows a flowchart for a very basic micrographic system. The annotations indicate that original documents are filmed on a rotary (*Ro*) camera at 24X onto 16mm silver (*S*) roll film, which is chemically processed (*chem*) at a speed of three meters per minute to produce a 1st generation, negative, silver (1NS) master reel as the working microform.

Figure 9-9 depicts a more complex hypothetical system in which the master reel is diazo-duplicated and then stripped-up as fiche; the fiche is, in turn, duplicated and distributed; and one duplicate fiche is encoded and placed in an automated retrieval device, from which it can be accessed in two forms: (a) a hard copy blowback, or (b) a screen image on a remote CRT display, via closed-circuit television. In the process, the master microforms in each duplicating set are filed for manual retrieval.

155

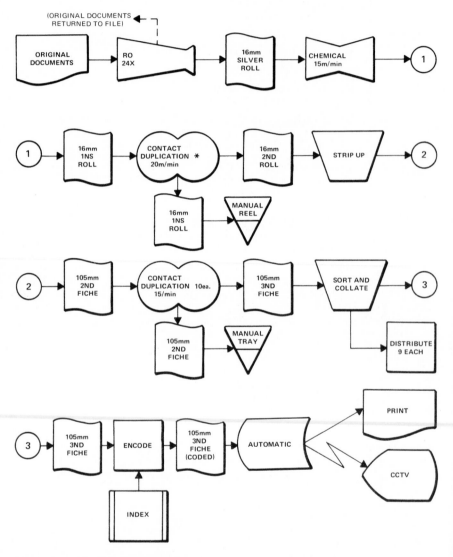

* Indicate number of duplicates made if more than one.

Fig. 9.9. A more complex system, requiring 13 of the 20 available flowchart symbols (excluding arrows). The depicted system is explained in the text.

Other examples of typical uses of the flowchart symbols may be found in Chapters 1 and 2, where they were used to depict actual systems designed to achieve various basic objectives.

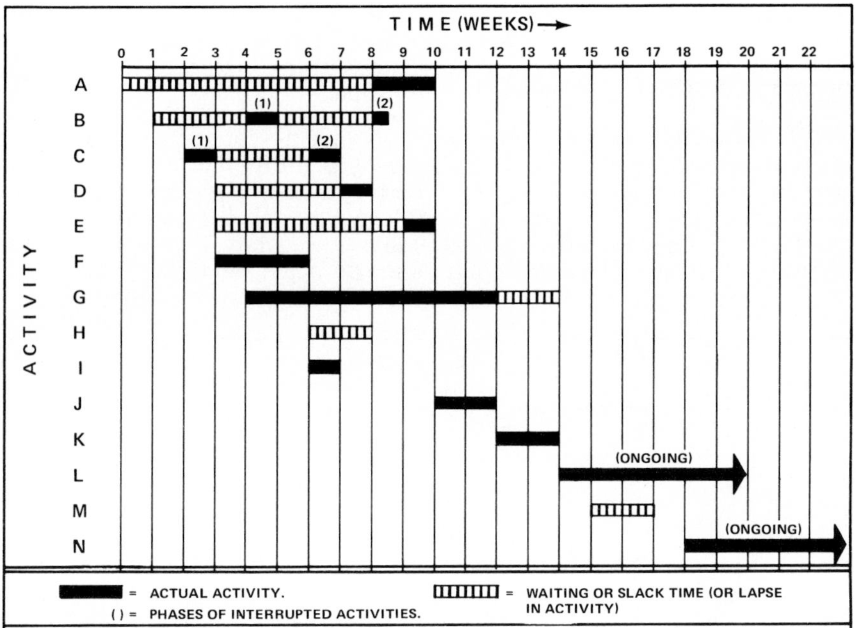

ACTIVITY DESCRIPTIONS:

A — Procurement of planetary camera -- allow 10 weeks lead time for delivery; 2 weeks for installation and testing.

B — Telephone installations -- from commencement to final installation of desk instruments, including lapse preceding furniture delivery. (Allow 3 weeks lead time for commencement.)

C — Special electrical wiring and plumbing -- from commencement to completion, including 3-week lapse during renovation.

D — Procurement of required furniture. Allow 4 weeks lead time for delivery; 2 — 3 days for setting up.

E — Procurement of mechanized file units, duplicators, printers, etc. -- allow 6 weeks lead time for delivery; 1 week for installation and testing.

F — Physical renovation of assigned space for production facilities and file.

G — Sorting and identifying original documents for microfilming -- 8 to 10 weeks.

H — Procurement of camera film for initial needs and of expendable materials as required for training purposes -- allow 2 weeks lead time for delivery.

I — Painting and other special detail work.

J — Indoctrination and training sessions for supervisors.

K — Indoctrination and training of clerical personnel; training of camera operator.

L — Commence microfilming.

M — Procure expendable supplies required for file operation; replenish camera film supply as required -- allow 2 weeks lead time for delivery.

N — Cut-over of file to micrographic operation. (This event marks completion of the project.)

Fig. 9.10. Bar (or Gantt) chart for a hypothetical micrographic system implementation schedule. The chart assumes that the affected documents are currently available on a paper basis. Activities include the initiation of orders for equipment and supplies, but not the analysis of bids or the awarding of contracts for plumbing, electrical work, etc.

VII Implementation Scheduling

In many instances, the system planner's job is not considered complete until he has seen the system through to successful implementation.

Although not a part of system design, *per se,* the advance charting of the various steps leading to implementation of a new system is a fairly common industrial engineering task that is sufficiently relevant to warrant a quick look before proceeding to the next topic.

Briefly, the two more common forms of implementation schedule are (1) a conventional bar chart, and (2) the so-called PERT (*Program Evaluation and Review Technique*) chart. Both are graphic devices that help ensure proper "dovetailing" of interdependent *parallel and sequential* activities leading eventually to full implementation of the system. Figure 9-10 shows a fairly typical bar—or *Gantt*—chart for the purpose, and Figure 9-11 shows the equivalent PERT chart. The system depicted is purely hypothetical.

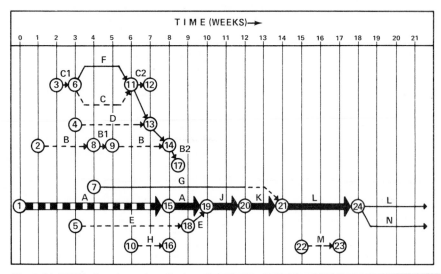

Fig. 9.11. PERT chart based on the bar chart in Fig. 9.10. The PERT chart rearranges the activities to provide a more schematic picture of how they interrelate. The bold path represents the practical minimum elapsed time to be allowed from commencement to completion of the entire project, and the "events" (circles) are numbered in the more or less logical sequence of their occurrence. For example, event 13 marks delivery of the office furniture, and event 14 marks both the completion of furniture installation and the commencement of installation of telephone sets on the desks.

The PERT chart illustrated is of the so-called *critical path* variety, the bold path through the center representing, in this example, the practical minimum total elapsed time from the placing of the first order to commencement of operation of the system. In the system depicted, incidentally, it is assumed that contracts, for electrical work, carpentry, etc., have already been awarded and that start and completion times have been established. Solid arrows indicate real activities, e.g., construction, installation, training, and are equivalent to the bold lines on the bar chart. Broken line arrows, corresponding to the broken lines on the bar chart, indicate "dummy activities", such as the elapsed time between ordering and delivery of hardware or supplies, or lapses between phases of a two-phase

158

job. Note that the commencement or resumption of some activities is dependent upon the completion of others.

The numbered circles on the PERT chart represent *events,* such as the commencement or completion of an activity. The numbers denote the more or less logical sequence in which the separate events should occur. Obviously, some of the events, though essentially independent and therefore separately numbered, will occur simultaneously.

In the example shown, the practical point of completion of implementation is at the end of the 18th week from commencement. Naturally, some activities, such as the microfilming of documents and the periodic ordering of expendable supplies, will continue past that point. Moreover, there will almost certainly be some post-completion "debugging" activities for the system planner to contend with.

VIII   Operational Considerations

In the course of designing a system, some thought naturally has to be given also to operational procedures and to problems that may be encountered in the daily operations of the system once it has been implemented. Operational considerations have already been touched upon briefly in the discussions of legal matters (Chapter 7), file maintenance, file security, quality control, and levels of labor. Also to be considered, however, are the protection of source documents and their preparation for microfilming; the proper operation and maintenance of in-house processors and duplicators; and the proper storage of microforms. All of these last-mentioned items are covered quite effectively in NMA Recommended Practice MS110-1974, "Operational Procedures for Production of Microforms."

Such matters as system management, logistics, budget, distribution and materials purchasing practices, etc., are, of course, outside the scope of this book and are perhaps best left to the intuitive skills of the individual system planner or manager.

Just one point bears brief mention in this regard, and that is the matter of where the responsibility should be placed for operation and maintenance of the system as a whole. In some companies, the inclination will be to divide the responsibility between two or more existing organizations. Others may establish a completely new organization for the purpose. Where COM is involved, the whole operation may be given to the EDP department to manage.

Though there is no single, hard-and-fast rule to cite, there are two things to bear in mind that may serve as guidance in deciding the matter: (1) by nature, a micrographic system, though it may employ computer technology, has little in common with data processing, since it is basically a reproduction system, and (2) experience has shown micrographic systems to function most smoothly when, from input to end product, all of the system functions are under the same organizational "umbrella".

* * *

In summary, this chapter has sought to identify and illustrate the many and varied facets of a specific system plan, and to show the inherent inter-

159

relationships of system elements: how the selection of one component will invariably influence that of another, or how several separate system considerations will combine to influence some basic system parameter, such as the physical space that must be alloted to the file. It has also sought to provide specific system design guidelines to the extent that it is practical to do so. Finally, it has sought to bring together the information from previous chapters, putting it all into perspective from the standpoint of designing an actual micrographic system to fill a specific need.

The next chapter will concern itself with the final step in the development of a micrographic system, short of actual implementation namely, the "selling" of the system to those who hold the purse strings.

Suggested Additional Reading

Auerbach on Computer Output Microfilm. New York, N.Y.: Auerbach Publishers, 1972. 160p.

Badler, Mitchell M., *1974-75 Microfilm Source Book.* New Rochelle, N.Y.: Microfilm Publishing, Inc., 1974. 224p.

Bagg, Thomas C., "Factors Dictating Characteristics of Systems Utilizing Microforms." *The Journal of Micrographics,* Spring, 1970. pp.143-146.

Barrett, W.J., *35mm Microfilming for Drawing Offices.* New York, N.Y.: Focal Press Ltd., 1970. 135p.

Ballou, Hubbard W., ed., *Guide to Micrographic Equipment.* Silver Spring, Md.: NMA, 1975. Vol.I, 256p.; Vol. II, 216p.; Vol. III, 80p.

Bolnick, Franklin I., "On-Line versus Off-Line COM Systems." *The Journal of Micrographics,* March/April 1971. pp.123-131.

Boyd, Sherman H., "Film Requirements for Computer Output Microfilm." *NMA Proceedings, 1972.* Silver Spring, Md.: NMA. pp. III-35—III-49.

Buffa, E.S., *Modern Production Management.* 3rd. edition. New York, N.Y.: John Wiley and Sons, 1969.
(Chapter 8, Network Planning Methods).

Evans, Frank B., *The Selection and Preparation of Records for Publication of Microfilm.* Washington, D.C.: U.S. National Archives, 1970. 14p.

Foster, Leslie H., "Effective Systems Design and Analysis for Large Scale Source Document Miracode Applications." *The Journal of Micrographics,* May/June 1974. pp.223-229.

Grey, Ben E., "The Skilled Personnel Shortage." *Reproduction Review and Methods,* May, 1974. pp.20,22.

Guide to Record Retention Requirements. Washington, D.C.: U.S. Government Printing Office, 1972. 91p.

Handbook of Hospital Microfilming. Westerly, R.I.: Arcata Microfilm, 1971. 20p.

Harmon, George H., "Integrating COM Into a Microfilm System." *The Journal of Micrographics,* July/August 1973. pp.261-263.

Harrison, Tom L., "CRT vs. COM—Real-Time vs. Real Enough Time." *The Journal of Micrographics,* September/October 1973. pp.37-44.

Harrison, Tom L., "Evaluating Microfilm Applications." *The Journal of Micrographics,* July/August 1972. pp.301-309.

Holmes, Donald C., *Determination of the Environmental Conditions Required in a Library for the Effective Utilization of Microforms.* Arlington, Va.: ERIC Document Reproduction Service, Computer Microfilm International Corp., 1970. (ED # 046 403).

How to Select a Reader or Reader-Printer. Silver Spring, Md.: NMA, 1974. 24p.

Information and Records Management. March 1975. (Three articles on the use of commercial storage centers).

Inspection and Quality Control of First Generation Silver Halide Microfilm. Silver Spring, Md.: NMA, 1972. 26p.

Kirk, Frank G., *Total System Development for Information Systems.* New York, N.Y.: Wiley-Interscience, 1973. 284p.

LaHood, Charles G., Jr., *Specifications for the Microfilming of Newspapers in the Library of Congress.* Washington, D.C.: Library of Congress, 1972. 24p.

Ling, Joseph T., "Photo Processing Wastes: What Needs To Be Done." *The Journal of Micrographics,* January/February 1975. pp.109-113.

Maynard, H.B., *Industrial Engineering Handbook.* 3rd. edition. New York, N.Y.: McGraw Hill, 1971.
(especially Section 8, Chapter 3, Graphical and Network Planning Techniques).

McKay, Mark, *A Guide to Microforms and Microform Retrieval Equipment.* Washington, D.C.: Applied Library Resources, Inc., 1972. 64p.

"Micrographics Forum: Guidelines to Handle Growth." *Modern Office Procedures,* April 1975. p.61.

Montouri, Theodore R., "Testing Recently Processed Microfilm for Archival Stability." *The Journal of Micrographics,* November/December 1974. pp.79-82.

Morgan, C.T., and others, *Human Engineering Guide to Equipment Design.* New York, N.Y.: McGraw Hill, 1963.
(especially Chapters 2,7,8, and 10).

Mottice, R., and M. Schreiber, "New Method for Residual Thiosulfate Analysis." *The Journal of Micrographics,* Fall 1969. pp.38-45.

NMA Standards: Quality for Computer Output Microfilm (MS1-1971); Format and Coding for Computer Output Microfilm (MS2-1971); Facsimile Transmission of Microfilmed Documents (MS3-1972); Flowchart Symbols and Their Usage in Micrographics (MS4-1972); Microfiche of Documents (MS5-1972); Microfilm Package Labeling (MS6-1974); Document Mark (Blip) Used in Image Mark Retrieval Systems (MS8-1974); Inspection and Quality Control of First Generation Silver Halide Microfilm (MS104-1972); Operational Practices Manual (MS110-1974).

Schreiber, Milton L., "New Residual Thiosulfate Test Methods." *The Journal of Micrographics,* September/October 1971. p.53.

Shworles, Thomas R., and Kalinsankar Mallik, "New Productive Capability and Earnings of Physically Disabled Homebound Persons." *The Journal of Micrographics,* May/June 1971. pp.223-231.

Smitzer, Louis A., "Toward Ultimate Quality Duplicate Microfilm." *The Journal of Micrographics,* September/October 1972. pp.27-31.

Stephan, Spray, "Methylene Blue Test." *The Journal of Micrographics,* May/June 1974. p.237.

Storage and Preservation of Microfilms. Kodak Pamphlet No. P-108. 1965.

Watson, Margaret, "Establishing a Micrographic Training Program: Rehabilitation/Industry Cooperation." *The Journal of Micrographics,* May/June 1975. pp.211-213.

Woodward, Thomas B., "Benefits of an Aperture Card System." *NMA Proceedings, 1974.* Silver Spring, Md.: NMA. pp. II-282—II-294.

Chapter 10

Selling the System

Analyzing an operation and formulating a detailed plan to make that operation more efficient can be a big job. But, no matter how thorough and painstaking the task, there is always one final, crucial step required to see it through to fruition—namely, convincing the right people that the necessary funds should be provided for implementation of the proposed system plan. In short, the system has to be developed, then "sold."

Recognizing that effective salesmanship is not a universal instinct, this chapter will attempt to lay down some basic guidelines to follow in mapping out the strategy for putting across a system proposal. All of the guidelines to be covered can be summed up in the following four questions:

1. At whom should the selling effort be directed?
2. What questions are likely to arise?
3. What are the essential points that must be made in outlining the system plan?
4. In what format should the proposal be presented?

Let's examine each of these questions for the answers that will help insure an effective system proposal.

I. Who to "Sell" to.

Some system planners maintain that the proposal should be presented directly to top management, who, if they are sold on it, will *decree* implementation of the new system. This approach circumvents those lower eschelon people who will be directly affected by the move and who might have been reluctant to go along with it because of a natural resistance to change. An opposing school of thought maintains that at least the supervisory level of the affected department(s) should be familiarized with the proposed system and their comments solicited before the plan is finalized, or that they should perhaps even be given some more direct role in the system planning. They will then be in a position to endorse the plan when it is presented to higher management.

This writer is inclined to subscribe to the latter view, for a couple of reasons. One is that a system is likely to work more smoothly if it hasn't been crammed down the throats of those most directly affected by its implementation. The other reason is that some constructive suggestions will invariably emerge from discussions with the people closest to the actual operation of the system. Such discussions may possibly even unearth a basic flaw in the system plan, or some vital consideration that has been inadvertently overlooked.

Depending on the nature of the system, it may even be advisable not to stop at the supervisory level in testing the system concept. As pointed out in Chapter 7, preliminary exposure of the prospective end users to the changes that confront them could be valuable in uncovering unforeseen problems at that level. In terms of strata within the organization, the user level could range all the way from the craftsman whose instructional manuals will now be in microform, to a high-ranking officer who will be receiving vital reports in microform instead of paper.

But, in any event, the decision to "go" has to come from those upper management echelons that control the necessary funds, and it is there, ultimately, that the most persuasive selling job has to be done. Let's analyze, therefore, what the people at the decision-making level will primarily be looking for in the proposal.

II. Likely Questions

"Why is this particular system being proposed at this time?" That is the logical first question to be anticipated in preparing the report, and inherent in that question are a couple of others: "What is the nature of the present system, and why is it unsatisfactory?", and "What alternatives were considered?"

The first ground to be covered by the proposal, therefore, is the present mode of operation and why it needs revision. Invariably, when a micrographic system is being considered, the present mode of operation involves the use of paper, and the reason for the proposed change is either that there is some recognizable problem or problems attributable to the use of paper, or that a knowledge of micrographic system capabilities has stimulated someone's thinking on how the present operation might be made more efficient.

An example of the first reason might be the recognition that micrographics offers potential advantages over paper in storage, retrieval, and distribution efficiency. It may even be that the present system does not involve the use of paper at all; it may be a system that uses on-line CRT display terminals for data retrieval, and perhaps it has been determined that the substitution of microform readers and COM-generated film will save considerable money, with at most only a slight reduction in retrieval time.

As for alternatives, possibly there were none to consider. But if there is even the remotest possibility that a workable alternative to the use of micrographics could improve an existing operation, the proposal should cover it and explain why it was rejected. Video tape is one possible example. Similarly, the proposal should anticipate questions on possible problems relating to the use of micrographic equipment, and should be presented so as to preclude them. For example, the question invariably arises as to whether wearers of bi-focal spectacles might have a problem using microform readers. Another question, where space-saving is cited as a major advantage of the micrographics approach, is whether the necessary new reproduction hardware (readers, printers, etc.) will not consume a good part of the space presumably saved.

Questions are also likely to arise about cost elements that may have been overlooked in the economic analysis preceding the system proposal. Where the proposal discusses economics, the material should be presented in a way that effectively precludes such questions. Make it clear that the economic analysis was thorough and accurate.

III. Essential Points

Besides describing the present system, explaining why it must be changed, and analyzing the alternatives considered, the proposal must clearly identify the new system's objectives and the advantages it offers over the present system. Obviously, one of the more effective selling points for any system is its potential to effect real savings, and that is, in fact, the basic objective of most system proposals.

Where a case for a new system is to be built on projected savings, the fact that the savings are *real,* as opposed to implicit, may not be enough. What particularly impresses management is *short-term* savings. In other words, if start-up costs are going to be heavy, recovery had better not be spread over too many years.

Fortunately, there is a degree of flexibility in the computation of annual costs, and, although the point was made in Chapter 8 that it is preferable to err on the high side, if you are going to err at all, in computing the annual cost of the system, it may be necessary to accept some risk in that regard if the system proposal is to stimulate sufficient interest at the upper echelons. The duration of the write-off period on the hardware investment is, after all, a matter of depreciation accounting and, as such, is determined primarily by the particular accounting philosophy to which one wishes to subscribe.

Let's remember, though, that any claims for significant savings in a system proposal have to be plausible, and that we have to be prepared to back them up if someone tries to shoot holes in them.

Other possible objectives of a proposed micrographic system might be:
1.   to gain space to permit lengthening of retention periods;
2.   to facilitate document retrieval to speed up turnaround on customer queries;
3.   to create a duplicate file as insurance against loss by disaster;
4.   to improve file integrity.

None of these are directly savings-related in an economic sense, but all are perfectly valid as objectives on which to sell a system.

Where the advantages are of a subtle nature, the significance of which may not be readily grasped by upper management, the chances of selling them the system are naturally reduced. It may be expedient in such instances to emphasize the case for hard savings in any way possible. For example, the main reason for considering a micrographic system for engineering drawings might be to minimize lost engineering time attributable to depletion of paper prints of the needed drawings. But engineering *time* is readily convertible to *dollars,* and it is on that very important fact that adoption of the system should be advocated.

If there are secondary advantages and indirect benefits to be derived from the system, apart from the principal objective(s), these should definitely be cited in the proposal. For example, a system intended primarily to preserve a rare historical document collection by establishing a microform duplicate collection, might also provide readier access to specific documents. Or a system intended primarily to speed up production of computer-generated reports by substitution of a COM recorder for a line printer might also significantly improve the efficency of subsequent distribution. The greater the number of advantages that can be cited, the easier the system should be to sell. *But make sure the advantages cited are realistic.*

Although by itself a weak selling point, the citing of *potential* advantages or savings can sometimes influence the acceptance of a system proposal. For example, the purchase of a COM device could be partially justified by the potential the device holds as a remote receiver of graphic information during idle periods. It could conceivably be arranged to work through the night, producing graphic film records from sporadic computer output that had been received via data links and taped during normal working hours. While perhaps not figuring in the immediate system plan, this potential supplementary application could be worth mentioning nonetheless.

Finally, the *end objective* of the system must not only be a practical one, but should be a pervading influence on every point made throughout the proposal. The kind of end objective to avoid is that of adopting micrographics, *per se,* simply because it is a more modern approach to information-handling, or because "everyone else is doing it." The fact that the use of micrographics is being proposed should be considered *secondary* to the end objective, which should strictly concern the need for improvement in present operations, or the realization of definite benefits from the adoption of a new capability.

IV. *Proposal Format*

In drafting a system proposal, it is well to be aware of some of the qualities that characterize the decision-makers who will be reading it. First, they are generally people who have got where they are because they have the knack to grasp the essence of a situation and to act accordingly with a minimum of deliberation. Secondly, they are busy and their time is therefore precious. And, thirdly, they tend to be skeptical, for an obvious reason: they stake their reputations and possibly their jobs on every decision they make, particularly where there are real economic risks involved.

From these characteristics, we can lay down the following basic ground rules for the preparation of a system proposal:
1.   be organized: first things first;
2.   be brief, but thorough;
3.   be convincing and accurate.
Let's examine each of these to see how best to achieve the desired effect.

1. *Organization*

Journalism students are taught a writing format called the *inverted pyramid,* in which the facts constituting a news story are arranged in a descending sequence from most important to least important. This gives the editor the advantage of gaining extra space for a late-breaking story simply by chopping off the ends (literally) of other stories. But, more important, it permits the *reader* to proceed as far into the story as he likes without having to worry about missing any of the essentials. In fact, in a well-written news story, all of the essentials, the "who, what, when, where, why, and how" of the story, are contained in the first one or two paragraphs.

In essence, the same format can apply to the writing of a system proposal. Although in practice, a proposal is not constructed like a news story, the same basic rule applies: *get the important facts up front, where they are sure not to be missed,* and save the details for later.

The way this is usually accomplished in a report or proposal is by preceding the actual text with an *abstract,* and that is definitely a recommended format. From there, the document may be organized in whatever way the writer finds most comfortable. But, whatever the order, it is good practice to make appropriate use of *headings and subheadings* so that the reader can quickly locate any particular aspect of the proposal. It follows that a table of contents at the beginning of the document will prove additionally useful.

The following list of basic sections of a typical proposal will serve as a guideline in organizing the final draft:
(a) *Introduction:* Tell the reader, briefly, what the proposal covers. *Note:* the introduction is separate from the abstract.
(b) *The Present System:* Describe, in appropriate detail the system that is being modified or replaced.
(c) *The Problem:* Why is the present system being reassessed at this time?
(d) *The Alternatives:* Give results of studies; discuss potential solutions that have been considered.
(e) *The Proposed System:* Describe.
(f) *Economics:* What will the new system cost?
(g) *Recommendations:* Funds to be appropriated, equipment to be purchased, implementation schedule, etc.

2. Brevity, Thoroughness

To be brief and thorough at the same time is to be *concise* or *succinct,* which means simply that all of the essential points are covered, but in the fewest possible words. This requires not only separation of the "wheat" from the "chaff" within a section, but also a knowledge of what is important to the ultimate reader: the decision-maker who has the power to accept or reject the proposal.

Of the list of sections presented above as guidelines, the first four—(a) through (d)—are really of an introductory nature and can be played down, if necessary, to keep the text of the proposal from becoming too long. The main points to be got across are *the nature of the system being proposed, what it will cost,* and *what is recommended in the way of action.*

Another way to keep the main body of the proposal as brief as possible without missing any of the essential points is to confine all of the details (statistical data, etc.) to separate attachments and appendices. In that way, the information is there if the reader wants to refer to it, but it doesn't obscure the essential points.

3. *Plausibility, Accuracy*

The object here is to penetrate the reader's skepticism, and the way to do that is to make doubly sure that you have an airtight case to present; that the proposal is both persuasive and realistic. In other words, not only must the proposed system excite interest and be worthy of consideration, but its alleged worthiness has to be substantially backed up by facts.

One thing to avoid is presenting a glowing picture of the system in the abstract without being able to back it up in the main text. At the other extreme, if the best that can be said in the abstract without stretching the truth is something like this, "There are indications that the system may produce moderate, long-term savings..." then you may as well reconsider submitting the proposal in the first place, unless, of course, there are overriding intangible benefits to be derived from the system's implementation.

Obviously, a more persuasive abstract would be one that confidently promises substantial, short-term savings from implementation of the proposed system. But, in any event, the abstract must accurately reflect the essence of the proposal, particularly with regard to size of investment and the anticipated time frame within which a net gain will be realized.

Following the guidelines presented in this chapter will not necessarily guarantee success in selling a micrographic system to upper management. Not only does that task involve personalities, and therefore psychological factors, but there are probably as many varying views on this single aspect of system planning as there are people who have successfully planned and "sold" systems.

Similarly, this book, in its entirety, is not a definitive work on the larger subject of system planning. As indicated at the outset, its objective is to provide guidelines to aid anyone who is relatively inexperienced at that task. Beyond what it has provided toward that end, there is plenty of room remaining for individual initiative and innovation.

Suggested Additional Reading

Hempel, Gardiner, "Managing and Marketing Microfilm Programs in the 1970s." *The Journal of Micrographics,* September/October 1972. pp.3-5.

Menkus, Belden, "How to Cost Out Microfilm." *Administrative Management,* May 1973. pp.37,40,42.

Reynolds, Carl H., "Selling COM to Management." *NMA Proceedings, 1974.* Silver Spring, Md.: NMA. pp. II-64—II-72.

Robertson, John R., "How to Sell Top Management on Microfilm Systems." *The Journal of Micrographics,* Summer 1970. pp.159-162.

Zarabet, Joseph, "Selling COM to Management." *Information and Records Management,* March 1973. pp. 46,48,50,52.

Appendix A
Glossary of Micrographics Terms

Most of the definitions that follow are the official ones, as published in NMA Industry Standard MS 100-1971, "Glossary of Micrographics." These are supplemented by the author's own definitions of terms that are (for the most part) not covered in the current edition of MS-100. The latter are designated with an asterisk (*).

A

acetate film (acetate base)
Safety film with a base composed principally of cellulose acetate or triacetate.

ammonia process
The development of two component diazo materials by immersing in a concentrated atmosphere of ammonia gas (NH_3). Development is achieved by alkalizing the acidic stabilizers in the diazo coating. (See diazo, two component.)

*analog
In an electronic graphic communication or conversion system, the representation of visual tonal variations at the input by proportional variations in the strength or frequency of an electrical current at the output.

antihalation undercoat (AHU)
A separate layer of light absorbing dye located between the emulsion and the base. During development of this film, the dye layer becomes transparent.

aperture
(1) In an optical system, an opening through which light can pass. This is frequently referred to as the "lens stop" or "lens opening" or "diaphragm".
(2) An aperture in a microreproduction system is a hole in a card which is specifically designed to hold a frame of microfilm.

---

* Author's definition (unofficial).

aperture card
A card with a rectangular hole or holes specifically prepared for the mounting or insertion of microfilm therein.

archival quality, archival standards
The degree to which a processed print or film will retain its characteristics during a period of use and storage. The ability to resist deterioration for a lengthy, specified time. See American National Standard PH4.8.

ASCII
American Standard Code for Information Interchange, X3.4 (also known as USASCII). An American National Standard binary coding scheme consisting of 128 seven bit patterns for printable characters and controls of equipment functions. An eight bit version of ASCII used by IBM is called ASCII 8. See American National Standard X3.4.

automatic coding
Index methods that are machine readable, i.e., digital or bit code.

azo dye
A moderately transparent dye which may be made dense visually by the reaction or coupling of a diazo and coupler. By exposure to light the dye may be made incapable of coupling in proportion to the exposure received.

B

background
The portion of a document drawing, microfilm, or print, which does not have line work, lettering, or other information.

background density
See density, background.

back lighting
Illumination which comes from behind the subject so as to provide trans-illumination.

base, film
The transparent plastic on which the photographic emulsion is coated. (See clear base and safety film.)

base density
The optical density of a film base. Since no plastic is 100% transparent, all films have some base density. The base density does not include any density produced by the emulsion layer.

BCD
Binary Coded Decimal Notation. Positional notation in which the individual decimal digits expressing a number in decimal notation are each

represented by a binary numeral, e.g., the number twenty-three is represented by 0010,0011 in the 8-4-2-1 type of binary coded decimal notation and by 10111 in binary notation.

BCDIC
Binary Coded Decimal Interchange Code. A six-bit computer code (permitting 64 codes) which became a de facto standard because of its use in earlier IBM computers, e.g., the IBM 705.

binary
A number system where quantities are represented in base 2 rather than base 10.

binary digital code
An optical pattern of clear and opaque rectangles machine encoded for random access retrieval used to index one or more images.

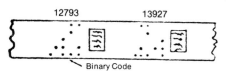

bit
A binary digit. In binary notation, either of the characters, 0 or 1. (See byte.)

blip
See document mark.

block
A set of things, such as words, characters, or digits handled as a unit.

*blowback
An enlarged print of a microimage.

bow
Departure from physical flatness across the width of film. (See curl.)

*"browsing"
In micrographics, the quick examination of one frame after another on a reader screen in the process of searching for a specific image on a multi-image microform.

byte
A sequence of adjacent bits operated upon as a unit and usually shorter than a word. (See bit.)

C

camera, planetary (flat-bed)
A type of microfilm camera in which the document being photographed

---
*Author's definition (unofficial).

and the film remain in a stationary position during the exposure. The document is on a plane surface at time of filming.

camera, rotary (flow)
A type of microfilm camera that photographs documents while they are being moved by some form of transport mechanism. The document transport mechanism is connected to a film transport mechanism, and the film also moves during exposure so there is no relative movement between the film and the image of the document.

camera, step and repeat
A type of microfilm camera which can expose a series of separate images on an area of film according to a predetermined format, usually in orderly rows and columns.

camera card
(1) An aperture card containing unexposed and unprocessed microfilm in an aperture in the card and which is to be exposed and processed while in the aperture of the card for the purpose of creating an image on the microfilm from a document.
(2) The unexposed and unprocessed card input of a processor-camera.

camera head
The portion of a microfilming machine which embodies the film, film advance mechanism and the lens. In planetary type machines, the camera head contains the shutter. In most rotary machines, there is no shutter, since exposures are made by intermittent illumination actuated by the document moving through the machine.

camera microfilm
First generation microfilm; also called the "master film".

camera-processor
See processor-camera.

card, EAM
See tabulating card.

card, image
(1) A card containing an image on exposed and processed microfilm which is secured in an aperture in the card.
(2) The exposed and processed output of: a mounter, a card-to-card printer, a roll-to-card printer or a processor-camera.

card, master data
A tabulating (EAM) card containing punched information (nonaperture). It is used in EAM machines to transfer the punched information or verify information in apertures, copy or image cards.

card column
One character position on an EAM card.

card feed
In EAM equipment, the path of the card from the hopper to the stacker.

card field
A column or group of columns on an EAM card allocated for punching specific information.

card-to-card printer
An equipment which produces duplicate card mounted microfilm by contact printing.

*carriage
On a microfiche or EAM image card (aperture card) reader or reproduction device, the "table" or "stage" onto which the microform is clamped, or into which it is inserted, at the image plane of the optical system. Sometimes also referred to as a "carrier."

carrier
(1) In xerography the substance in the developer which conveys a toner, but does not itself become a part of the viewable record.
*(2) as relating to a reader or printer component, see carriage.
* (3) as relating to an image-bearing medium, see Unit carrier.

cartridge
(1) A container enclosing processed microforms, designed to be inserted into readers, reader-printers and retrieval devices; used with a single core for roll microfilm.
(2) (deprecated) A light tight container protecting sensitized materials and facilitates while loading and unloading a camera, printer or processor; used with a single core for roll microfilm.

cassette
A double core container enclosing processed roll microfilm designed to be inserted into readers, reader-printers and retrieval devices.

* CCTV (Closed Circuit Television)
A television system in which the send and receive terminals are interconnected via dedicated communication circuits; usually confined to relatively short transmission distances, e.g., within a building, between buildings within a complex, intracity. CCTV systems for document transmission are generally of a higher resolution than commercial TV, and therefore may require wider bandwidth transmission channels.

character
One of a set of elements which may be arranged in ordered groups to express information. Each character has two forms:
(1) A human-readable form, graphic alphanumerics.
(2) A computer-readable form, coded alphanumerics consisting of a group of binary digits (bits).

character generator
The electronic portion of a device such as a COM which converts electrical signals to visible characters. (See Charactron Tube, stroke generator, and dot matrix.)

---

*Author's definition (unofficial).

173

character transfer rate
The rate at which characters are transferred from one place to another, e.g., magnetic tape to computer, computer to magnetic tape, computer to microfilm, etc.

chip
A unit of microfilm containing a micro image or images and coded identification. Chips are usually used in automatic retrieval systems and are most often 35 mm in width by three inches in length or less.

Ciné (motion picture) oriented images (IA orientation)
Jargon used with intent to reference images oriented on microfilm as follows, otherwise known as IA orientation.

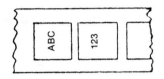

See American National Standard PH5.3, IA oriented images in Fig. 1.

code
The unique bit configuration describing a symbol or character.

code line
A visual index consisting of an optical pattern of clear and opaque bars parallel with the long edge of the microfilm, located between image areas.

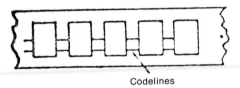

Codelines

*collective
As applied to microimage recording on multiimage microforms such as reels or fiche, the inclusion of relatively unrelated images or sets of images within a unit carrier. The converse of unitized—or unit—microimage recording.

column
(1) The part of a planetary camera which projects vertically from the base and which supports the camera head above the object being photographed.
(2) A vertical series of images on a microfiche or micro-opaque card.
(3) See card column.

COM
(1) Computer Output Microfilm: microfilm containing data produced by a recorder from computer generated electrical signals.

---
* Author's definition (unofficial).

(2) Computer Output Microfilmer: a recorder which converts data from a computer into human readable language and records it on microfilm.

(3) Computer Output Microfilming: a method of converting data from a computer into human readable language onto microfilm.

Comic strip oriented images (IB orientation)
Jargon used with intent to reference images oriented on microfilm as follows, otherwise known as IB orientation.

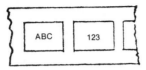

See American National Standard PH5.3, IB oriented images in Fig. 1.

computer graphics
Drawings, patterns and graphs produced by a computer on paper, microfilm or the screen of a CRT.

contact printing
A method of printing in which the unexposed stock is held in direct contact with the master or intermediate bearing the image to be copied.

continuous tone copy
Photographic copy which contains a varying gradation of gray densities between black and white.

contrast
(1) An expression of the relationship between the high and low brightness of a subject or beween the high and low density of a photographic image.

(2) The rate of density change or the density change per unit exposure. A photographic image is said to have high contrast if the difference between the maximum and minimum density is great. Sensitized materials are graded from "hard" (high contrast) to "soft" in accordance with their inherent contrast characteristics.

conventional processing
Conventional processing of silver halide films denoting a processing sequence of development, fix (or monobath), wash, and dry. For diazo film, it denotes processing in an alkaline (ammonia) environment. For vesicular and dry silver films it denotes processing by heat.

conversion, image
The operation or function of transferring or reproducing microimages from one stage in a microfilm system to the next.

copy
(1) Noun—Duplicate (deprecated in that sense). The product obtained from reproducing an original.

(2) Verb—To reproduce an original by hand or by machine.

copyboard
A flat, level structure used to support documents in the photographic field.

copy card
(1) An aperture card containing unexposed and unprocessed microfilm which will be exposed and processed for the express purpose of duplicating or reproducing a microimage.
(2) The unexposed input of a card-to-card printer or roll-to-card printer.

core
(1) The center portion of a reel, spool, cartridge, magazine or cassette. A cassette has two cores.
(2) An unflanged, cylindrical form on which film or paper is wound. See American National Standard PH1.13.

corner cut
On aperture cards and microfiche, a diagonal cut at the corner of a card as a means of identification of the photosensitive side of the film.

CPU
Central Processing Unit. A unit of a computer that includes the circuits controlling the interpretation and execution of instructions.

Crabtree Test (Ross Crabtree)
See residual thiosulfate test.

*CRT (Cathode Ray Tube)
An electronic imaging device in which an electron beam is accelerated within a vacuum to strike a phosphorescent screen with sufficient force to cause fluorescence at the point of impact. By a combination of electronic deflection and gating (and possibly matrixing), the beam can be caused to "write" characters or lines on the screen.

curl
Departure from physical flatness in the length of film or paper. To tend to roll up. See American National Standard PH1.29. (See bow.)

D

* data base
A term used to apply to the totality of data (including printed text and pictures) constituting a file, collection, library, etc., or a given segment thereof.

deck
A set of tabulating (EAM) cards.

densitometer
A device used to measure the optical density of an image or base by measuring the amount of incident light reflected or transmitted.

---

* Author's definition (unofficial).

density, background
The opacity of the non-information area of an image. (See density, optical.)

density, diffuse transmission
Diffuse transmission density is expressed as the common logarithm of the ratio of the radiant flux striking the sample (perpendicular to its surface) to the radiant flux transmitted by the sample when all the transmitted flux is collected and equally evaluated, i.e., all the emerging rays have the same effect on the receiver regardless of the angle at which they emerge.

density, line
The opacity of the line work, letters, or other non-background information of an image. (See density, optical.)

density, maximum (d-max)
(1) The density of an unexposed diazo material after complete development.
(2) The density of a silver halide material attained by complete exposure and complete development.

density, minimum (d-min)
The lowest density obtainable in a processed film. (See burn-out.)

density, optical
The light-absorbing quality of a photographic image (degree of opacity of film and blackness for paper prints) usually expressed as the logarithm of the opacity. Several specific types of density values for a photograph may be expressed but diffuse transmission density is the one of greatest use in the case of microfilm and diffuse reflection density is generally of interest for paper prints. See American National Standards PH2.17 and PH 2.19.

density, packing
The number of useful storage cells per unit of dimension; e.g., the number of bits per inch stored on a magnetic tape or drum track. (See bit.)

depth of field
The distance between the points nearest and farthest from the camera which are acceptably sharp, at a given lens setting.

depth of focus
The allowable tolerance in lens-to-film distance within which an acceptably sharp image of the subject focused upon can be obtained.

desk top reader
A small microfilm reader which can be placed on top of a desk and generally occupies about one square foot or less. (See reader.)

develop
To subject to the action of chemical agents (as in xerography) for the purpose of bringing to view the invisible or latent image produced by the action of light on a sensitized surface.

developer
(1) A chemical reagent used to produce a visible image on an exposed photographic layer. It may take many forms for different materials, such as conventional formulae for silver emulsions, plain water used to develop blueprints; or a gas, such as ammonia vapor used to develop diazo films and prints.
(2) A physical material, or mixture of physical materials used to develop a latent xerographic image.

diazo material
A slow print film or paper, sensitized by means of diazonium salts, which subsequent to exposure to light strong in the blue to ultraviolet spectrum and development forms an image. Diazo material generally produces nonreversible images, i.e., a positive image will produce a positive image and a negative image will produce a negative image.

diffuse transmission density
See density, optical, diffuse transmission.

*digital
In an electronic graphic communication or conversion system, the representation of visual tonal variations (and perhaps their relative locations as well) at the input by binary "code words," or groups of on-off electrical pulses, at the output.

*digital data compression
In an electronic graphic communication or conversion system, the detection and encoding of black-white transitions in a graphic image in a way that differentiates between essential image elements and wasted space. (Also sometimes referred to as Redundancy Reduction.)

direct image film
A film that will retain the same polarity as the previous generation or the original material; that is, tone for tone, black for black, white for white, negative for negative, or positive for positive with conventional procession. (See polarity).

distribution copies
Microfilm copies, usually second or third generation, produced from camera microfilm or intermediates for distribution to points of use.

document
A written, typed or printed paper.

document mark (blip)
An optical mark, usually rectangular, within the recording area, and usually below the image on a roll of microfilm used for counting images or frames automatically.

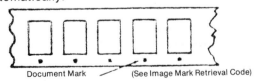

Document Mark   (See Image Mark Retrieval Code)

---

* Author's definition (unofficial).

document retrieval systems
Document retrieval systems go one step further than reference retrieval systems and provide a complete copy of the document instead of just a citation or reference. (See reference retrieval.)

dot matrix
A method of generating characters utilizing a matrix of dots, each of which may be independently turned on or off and the combination thereof producing a human-readable character.

drawing
(1) An original pencil, ink or typewritten line and/or lettered representation which is drawn on a suitable transparent or translucent material.
(2) A reproduced tracing.

dry silver film
A non-gelatin silver film which is developed by application of heat.

duo
A term used to define an image-positioning technique in rotary camera microfilming. One half of the film is masked and images are photographed along the exposed half of the film. When the full length of film has passed through the camera, it is reloaded so that a second series of images is photographed on the side previously left unexposed. See American National Standard PH5.3.

duplex
(1) Photographic paper having emulsion coating on both sides
(2) A term used to define an image-positioning technique in rotary camera microfilming. Through the use of mirrors or prisms, an image of the front side of a document is photographed on one half of the film while an image of the back side of the same document is photographed simultaneously on the other half of the film. See American National Standard PH5.3.
(3) A term applied to any camera capable of performing duplex work as described in (2) above.

duplicate
(1) Noun—In microcopying, a copy usually made by contact printing from a master or an intermediate.
(2) Verb—To make multiple copies of a document, usually with the aid of a master.

dye-back film
Any film having a light-absorbing dye coating on the base side of the film to improve daylight loading characteristics and to reduce halation. The dye must be removed during processing.

E

EAM
Electrical Accounting Machine.

179

EAM Card
See EAM and Tabulating Card.

EBCDIC
Extended Binary Coded Decimal Interchange Code. An eight-bit computer code (permitting 256 codes) which became a de facto standard because of its use in later IBM computers, e.g., the IBM S/360.

* edge-notching
A system of coding unit microforms for automated retrieval by cutting a pattern of notches along one edge (usually the bottom with respect to the position of the microform as filed), or, alternatively, by affixing a pre-notched clip to one edge of the microform.

EDP
Electronic Data Processing.

eight-up format
A 35mm microfilm format which permits eight 8-1/2 x 11 inch (approximately) documents to be filmed within a single microfilm frame.

emulsion
A single or multi-layered coating of gelatinous material on a transparent base carrying radiant energy reactive chemicals that create a latent image upon exposure. Processing techniques produce a final, visible, useable image.

emulsion numbers
Numbers used by photographic film and paper manufacturers to identify coating data.

enlargement ratio
The ratio of the linear measurement of a microimage of a document to the linear measurement of the enlarged image, expressed as 20X, 30X, etc.

enlarger-printer
A machine which projects an enlarged image from microfilm, develops, and fixes the image on a suitable material.

exposure
(1) The act of exposing a light-sensitive material to a light source.
(2) A section of a film containing an individual image, as a roll containing six exposures.
(3) The time during which a sensitive surface is exposed, as an exposure to two seconds.
(4) The product of light intensity and the time during which it acts on the photo-sensitive material.

---

* Author's definition (unofficial).

F

facsimile
(1) An exact copy of an original document.
(2) The process or result of the process by which fixed graphic images are scanned, transmitted electronically, and reproduced either locally or remotely.

fiche
See microfiche.

field
(1) The area covered or "seen" by the lens of a camera.
(1) See card field and card subfield.

file
In information retrieval systems, the master repository of information, generally an ordered file of microforms designed for convenient access by a predetermined means.

film
Any sheet or strip of transparent plastic coated with a light-sensitive emulsion.

film, master
The camera microfilm. It is also known as the original film.

film, nonperforated
Roll film which does not have sprocket holes or perforations.

film, nonreversing (direct positive)
Film which does not change from positive to negative images or vice versa in successive generations, for example diazo film.

film, perforated
Roll film having sprocket holes accurately located along one or both edges to aid in transporting and positioning the film for successive exposures in a camera.

film, processed
Film which has been exposed to suitable radiation and has been treated to produce a fixed or stabilized visible image.

film, reversal
A film which after exposure is specially processed to produce a positive image instead of the customary negative image.

film, silver
A film which is coated with a silver halide emulsion.

film advance
(1) The movement of film across the exposure area of a camera in regular increments for successive frames.
(2) The length of film moved after a given exposure. (See pull-down.)

fine-grain
(1) Descriptive of film emulsions in which the grain size is small. The term is relative as there is a wide variation in grain size among various fine-grain films.

first generation image
The picture of a document, generally used as a master, produced directly by the camera.

fixer
A solution used to remove undeveloped silver halides from photo-sensitized emulsions. The fixer usually contains sodium or ammonium thiosulfate (hypo), a hardening agent, and an acid or acid salt.

flash card
A target, generally printed with distinctive markings, which is photo-graphed to facilitate indexing of film. (See flash index, indexing film.)

flow camera
See camera, rotary.

focal plane
The surface (plane) on which an axial image transmitted by a lens is brought to sharpest focus; the surface occupied by the light-sensitive film or plate in a camera.

focus
(1) The plane in which rays of light reflected from a subject converge to form a sharp image of the original after passing through different part of a lens.
(2) To adjust the relative positions of the lens and film to obtain the sharpest possible image.

fog
Nonimage photographic density. The defect is due to the action of stray light, improperly compounded processing solutions, or wrongly stored or outdated photographic materials.

font
A family of compatible assortment of characters of a given size and style. (See microfont and OCR-B.)

forms flash (forms overlay)
The method by which document formats are superimposed on a frame of computer output microfilm containing other data.

frame (film frame)
The area of a photographic film exposed to light in a camera during one exposure, regardless of whether or not this area is filled by the document image. (See code area, image area, and recording area.)

frame, microfiche
(1) One microimage and margin contained within a film frame. (See margin.)
(2) A single area of a grid pattern.

generation
A measure of the remoteness of a particular copy from the original material. The picture taken of a document, cathode ray tube, etc. is termed first generation microfilm (camera microfilm). Copies made from this first generation are second generation, and copies from the second generation are third generation, etc. First generation negative appearing microfilm is designated 1N and second generation positive appearing microfilm is designated 2P, etc. (See N, P, negative appearing image, positive appearing image.)

generation, even
The second, fourth, sixth, etc. generations are even.

generation, odd
The first, third, fifth, etc. generations are odd.

grain
(1) The discrete particles of image silver in photographs. The random distribution of these particles in an area of uniform exposure gives rise to the appearance of clumping known as "graininess".
(2) The direction of transport in the paper-making machine which usually curls more with the grain than "against" or across the grain. (See grain direction, length direction and width direction.)

graphic
Of, or pertaining to, data in the form of pictorial communications, as for example, drawings, charts, engineering designs and plotted data.

grid gauge
An inspection tool which is used to check the position of images on microfiche.

grid, microfiche
A defined array of horizontal and vertical lines which divide an area into uniform space called frames. The grid defines the arrangement of the rows and columns of microimages.

H

halation
A halo ghost image or fog caused by reflection of rays of light from the base to the emulsion or by internal scattering of light within the film.

hand viewer
A small, portable magnifying device used for viewing microfilm. Magnification generally ranges from 5X to 15X.

hard copy
An enlarged copy usually on paper.

high reduction (hr)
Reductions above 30X up and inclusive of 60X.

Hollerith
Binary coded information representing alphanumeric or special characters. Normally, Hollerith is used to denote characters punched in standard eighty-column EAM cards.

hypo
Ammonium or sodium thiosulfate. The agent used to remove unexposed silver halides from silver emulsion film. The term is generally used to refer to a fixer solution which may contain also certain acids and/or hardening agents.

hypo, residual
The amount of ammonium or sodium thiosulfate (fixer) that remains in film or paper after washing.

hypo eliminator
A chemical solution which assists in the removal of hypo from films or prints.

hypo test
A method of checking the amount of residual hypo remaining in a film or print after washing. (See residual thiosulfate test.)

I

image
A representation of an object such as a document or other information sources produced by light rays.

image, latent
The invisible image produced by the action of radiant energy on a photosensitive surface. It may be made visible by the process of development.

image, latent electrostatic
The electrostatic charge pattern remaining on a photoconductor after exposure to radiant energy, or created on an insulating medium by electrostatic techniques. It may be made visible by the process of xerographic development.

image, negative
A photographic image in which the values of light and dark of the original subject are inverted. In a negative, light objects are represented by high densities and dark objects are represented by low densities.

image plane
See focal plane.

image, positive
A photographic image in which the values of light and dark of the original subject are represented in their natural order. In a positive, light objects are represented by low densities and dark objects are represented by high densities.

184

image area
Part of the recording area reserved for the image.

impact printer
An output unit which mechanically prints or typewrites characters, usually on paper.

Indexing film
A system using targets, flash cards, lines, or bars, etc., for locating information appearing on a reel of microfilm. It enables rapid location of the section of film which contains the desired image on the reel without the necessity of examining each image sequentially.

indexing, visual
See indexing film.

information area
The area of a document which contains information usually exclusive of the margin.

insert, film
A microfilm strip cut in lengths to fit a jacket, film holder or for stripping up a master microfiche.

intermediate
A microfilm or other reproducible used to make distribution copies; microfilm intermediates are usually made from camera microfilm.

interpreter
An EAM card machine which senses a punched card and prints the information on that card.

interpreting
The printing of information on the same EAM card in which it is punched.

J

jacket
A transparent plastic carrier with a single or multiple sleeve or pocket made to hold microfilm in flat strips.

jacket, notched
Special acetate pockets with a die-cut edge to facilitate film strip insertion.

jacket rib
The thin narrow plastic strips which separate acetate sheets thereby forming the sleeves or pockets.

jacket set
The curved shape which may be taken by jackets after aging.

K

Kalvar®
A trademark for the film and equipment products of the Kalvar Corporation.

keypunching
The cutting of coded holes in tabulating (EAM) cards.

L

laminate
Material made up of two or more layers bonded together, usually with an adhesive.

lap reader
A microfilm reader less than 4 kg. in mass (less than 8.8 lbs.). (See reader.)

latent image
See image, latent.

latent image fade
The fading of a latent image on a film which is not developed immediately after exposure. The amount and rate of fading depends on time, temperature, humidity storage conditions, and type of emulsion.

latitude
A term indicating the range of exposure over which a sensitized material will yield an acceptable reproduction. It is usually related to the length and slope of the straight line portion of the characteristic curve.

leader
Film at the beginning of a roll which is used for the threading of a camera, projector, and processing machine.

led
Light-emitting diode.

light, terms of
brightness—
(1) An effect upon visual sensation that enables an observer to detect differences in luminance.
(2) A photometric measure of light emission per unit of a luminous body or a translucent or reflecting surface.
candela—The International Standard unit of luminous intensity.
diffused—Light which does not reach the subject in a single beam, but is scattered by a medium such as clouds, ground glass, spun glass, or thin fabric.
foot lambert—A unit of brightness, equal to the uniform brightness of a perfectly diffusing surface emitting or reflecting light at the rate of one lumen per square foot.

illumination—A term synonomous with flux density but stated in terms of units of luminous flux incident upon a unit area.

lumen—The unit of luminous flux; the flux emitted through a unit solid angle (one steradian) from a point source of one candle.

luminance—The luminous intensity per unit area of a light source, or luminous flux per unit solid angle per unit area projected upon a plane perpendicular to the direction specified. Sometimes called photometric brightness.

lux—A unit of illuminance, lumen per square meter.

light box
A device for inspecting film, which provides diffused illumination evenly dispersed over the viewing area.

light-sensitive
Materials which undergo changes when exposed to light. The commonly used photographic light-sensitive materials used in films and paper are the silver halides, diazo dyes, bichromated gelatin, and the photoconductive materials used in xerography.

light-struck
The production of a latent image on photosensitive material usually by accidental exposure to light.

*logic
The pre-planned, automatic series of steps by which an electronic or mechanical controlling device achieves its purpose.

low reduction (lr)
Reductions up to and inclusive of 15X.

M

magnetic tape
A ribbon of paper, metal or plastic, coated or impregnated with magnetic material on which information may be stored in the form of magnetically polarized areas.

magnification range
The lineal range or span of magnification in a given optical system which is usually expressed in diameters or times, i.e., magnification range 12X through 24X.

margin (drawings)
(1) On drawings, the area of the drawing beyond the line enclosing the information area.
(2) On a film frame, the area of background between the edge of the drawing and the edge of the film frame is sometimes called margin.

margin, microfiche
The non-image area outside the margins of the document but within the frame.

master
A copy of a document, or in some processes the original itself from which copies can be made.

---

*Author's definition (unofficial)

master film
Any film, but generally the camera microfilm, used to produce further reproductions, as intermediates or distribution copies.

*McBee Keysort
A manual system of file card retrieval in which sets of cards are "skewered" on a metal rod via a set of holes representing a given information element. By jogging, the cards containing the desired information will be liberated from the pack because that particular "hole" on the applicable cards is shaped to permit easy release from the rod.

measuring magnifier
A magnifier with a scale in the object plane used for measurement and comparison purposes.

medium reduction (mr)
Reductions above 15X up to and inclusive of 30X.

*methylene blue
A chemical dye used in the testing of archival permanence of processed microimages.

microcopy
A copy obtained by photography in a size too small to be read without magnification.

*microfacsimile
The transmission and/or reception of microimages via facsimile communication. See facsimile, definition (2).

microfiche
A sheet of microfilm containing multiple microimages in a grid pattern. It usually contains a title which can be read without magnification.

microfilm
(1) A fine-grain, high resolution film containing an image greatly reduced in size from the original.
(2) The recording of microphotographs on film.
(3) Raw film with characteristics as in (1).

microfilm card
A general term for camera cards, copy cards, image cards and aperture cards.

microfilmer
See camera.

microfont
An upper case charter font designed by NMA specifically for microfilm applications.

microform
A generic term for any form, either film or paper, which contains microimages.

---

*Author's definition (unofficial)

micrographics
(1) The industry which reduces any form of information to a microform medium.
*(2) A term applied to the use of microimage recording, retrieval, and reproduction technologies in an information system.

*micrographic system
An information system that utilizes the special advantages of micro-imaging in the areas of space saving, reproducibility, durability, file integrity, and automated retrieval.

microimage
A unit of information, such as a page of text or a drawing, too small to be read without magnification.

*microimaging
The process of optically reducing a document onto film or other image recording media to a degree that it is rendered unreadable without magnification. Distinguished from ordinary photography mainly by its higher precision in terms of preservation of image detail.

*micromire
An array of 10X-reduced ISO *Mire #1* legibility test charts. See *Mire.*

micro-opaque
A sheet of opaque material bearing one or more microimages.

microphotography
The application of photographic processes to produce copy in sizes too small to be read without magnification. (Not to be confused with photo-micrography.)

microprint
Microimages on opaque stock, produced by printing as distinct from microimages produced on a photosensitive material.

micropublishing
To issue new (not previously published) or reformatted information, in multiple copy microform for sale or distribution to the public. (See microrepublishing, duplicating.)

microreproduction
(1) Copy rendered in sizes too small to be read without magnification and which is produced photographically or by other means on either transparent or opaque materials.
(2) The process of making microimages.

microrepublishing
To re-issue material previously or simultaneously published in hard copy form in multiple copy microform for sale or distribution to the public. (See micropublishing, duplicating.)

military "D"
The term given to the DOD specified aperture size and location in (EAM) tabulating cards.

---
*Author's definition (unofficial)

*mire
> French for *test chart*. The ISO *Mire #1* is the basic microcopy legibility test standard in several countries outside the U.S.

*modularity
> A design concept in which flexibility, of capacity, versatility, etc. is provided for in a system or stand-alone device by the ability to conveniently add or remove discrete supplemental units in "building block" fashion.

monobath
> A single solution combination developing and fixing bath for processing photographic materials.

mounter
> A device for simultaneously cutting, positioning, and fastening film frames in aperture cards.

multi-frame document
> See sectioning.

N

NBS chart
> See resolution test pattern.

negative appearing image
> A photographic image with light lines, characters, and neutral tones on a dark background.

nonperforated film
> See film, nonperforated.

O

*OCR (Optical Character Recognition)
> An electronic system by which printed or photographically recorded characters can be rapidly recognized by a combination of scanning techniques and electronic logic, and converted to binary digital codes for storage, transmission, etc.

*odometer
> On a roll microform reader, a visual indicator of an approximate image address. An integral part of the reader, usually mechanical and similar in operation to the cumulative mileage register on an automobile speedometer. Used in conjunction with a microfilmed or external index.

off-line
> (1) Pertaining to equipment or devices not under direct control of the central processing unit, i.e., a COM.
> (2) Pertaining to equipment or devices not directly linked to a COM, i.e., processor, enlarger, etc.

---

*Author's definition (unofficial)

opacity
The characteristic of a material which prevents light from passing through it.

opaque screen
A reader screen of opaque material on which an image is produced by reflected light.

*optical path
The path followed by the light rays in an optical system. In addition to the image to be viewed or reproduced, physical components within the path may include lenses, prisms, mirrors and an image-forming surface. All of the latter serve to control the shape, direction, total length, etc. of the optical path. (See Optical system.)

optical system
The optical system includes all the parts of a photographic lens and accessory optical elements which are designed to contribute to the formation of an image on the photographic emulsion or on a screen for viewing.

original
The document from which copies are produced.

overdevelop
To permit a photographic image to be developed too much because of one or more of the following factors:
(1) Excessive time.
(2) Excessive temperature.
(3) Overstrength of developer solution.
(4) Excessive agitation.

overexpose
To permit too much exposure of a photographic copy. This may be caused by:
(1) Light too brilliant.
(2) An aperture too large.
(3) Exposure time too long.

P

packing density
See density, packing.

pagination
A term referring to the arrangement of pages or microimages of pages on a microfilm or micro-opaque.

*"pantograph"
As applied loosely to microfiche readers, a simple "tracking" or "following" mechanism that brings a specific page image to the screen by manually moving a pointer to the desired coordinate location on a replica of the fiche grid.

---

*Author's definition (unofficial)

paper, heavy weight
Sensitized photographic paper with average thickness limits of above 0.483mm (0.0190 inches). See American National Standard PH1.1.

paper, lightweight (standard weight—document weight)
Sensitized photographic paper with average thickness limits of above 0.109 to 0.150mm (0.0043 to 0.0059 inches) inclusive. See American National Standard PH1.1.

paper, medium weight
Sensitized photographic paper with average thickness limits of above 0.211 to 0.282mm (0.0083 to 0.0111 inches) inclusive. See American National Standard PH1.1.

paper, ultra thin (extra lightweight)
Sensitized photographic paper with average thickness limits of above 0.056 to 0.079mm (0.0022 to 0.0031 inches) inclusive. See American National Standard PH1.1.

peripheral
Near the boundary or edge of the field of an optical system; the outer fringe.

photoconductor
(1) A material which is an electrical insulator in darkness but which becomes electrically conductive when exposed to light.
(2) A material which will hold an electrical charge in the dark but which is dissipated when illuminated.

photocopy
A photographic reproduction, excluding microcopy, generally produced by exposing the image of an original on photographic film or paper.

photocopying
The application of photographic processes to produce copies, excluding microcopies, generally by exposing the image of an original on photographic film or paper.

photosensitive
Sensitivity to light.

plane, document
That surface or area in space at which the document is positioned during exposure.

plane, film
See focal plane.

planetary camera
See camera, planetary.

platen
A mechanical device which holds the film in the focal plane during exposure.

point light source
See light, point source.

polarity
A word used to indicate the change or retention of the dark to light relationship of an image, i.e., a first generation negative to a second generation negative indicates the polarity is retained.

polyester
Transparent plastic used as a film base because of its transparency, stability and relative non-inflammability.

positive appearing image
A photographic image with dark lines, character, and neutral tones on a light background.

print
(1) Noun—A reproduction or copy on photographic film or paper.
(2) Verb—To produce a reproduction or copy on photographic film or paper.

print film
A fine grain, high resolution film used primarily for making contact film copies.

printer, contact
An exposing device containing a light source and a means for holding a film in close contact with the sensitized material on which the print is made.

processing
The treatment of exposed photographic material to make the latent image visible, i.e., a series of steps consisting of developing, fixing, washing, and drying.

processor
Any machine which performs the various operations necessary to process photographic material.

processor-camera
A device which has both the functions of a processor and a camera.

projection
(1) Formation of an image through optical means onto a sensitized surface or viewing screen, usually in magnified size.
(2) An image that is visible after it has been optically projected through space onto a surface.

pull-down
The length of film advanced after each exposure.

R

raw stock
Unexposed, unprocessed sensitized material.

reader
A projection device for viewing an enlarged microimage with the un-aided eye.

reader-printer
A machine which combines the functions of a reader and an enlarger-printer.

rear projection
The projection of an image onto a translucent screen from the side opposite to that from which the image is viewed.

records preparation
The process of sorting, flattening, removing fasteners (such as staples and paper clips), and index planning preliminary to microfilming.

reduction
A measure of the number of times a given linear dimension of an object is reduced when photographed, expressed as 16X, 24X, etc.

reduction, effective
A measure of the number of times an imaginary document would have been reduced to equal the size of the COM generated microimage, expressed as 24X, 30X, etc.

reduction ratio
The ratio of the linear measurement of a document to the linear measurement of the image of the same document expressed as 16:1, 20:1, etc.

reel
A flanged holder on which processed roll film is wound, designed to be inserted into readers, reader-printers and retrieval devices. See American National Standard PH5-6.

reflectance target
A test target which has a known fixed percentage of reflectivity.

reproduction (of a document)
The action of copying or duplicating a document.

residual thiosulfate (residual hypo)
Ammonium or sodium thiosulfate (hypo) remaining in film or paper after washing. Since residual hypo has a deleterious effect and reduces per-manence, careful control must be maintained in processing to ensure that permissible limits are not exceeded. (See archival quality.)

resolution
The ability of optical systems and photo-materials to render visible fine detail of an object: a measure of sharpness of an image, expressed as the number of lines per millimeter, discernible in an image. Resolution in processed microfilm is a function of film emulsion, exposure, camera lens, camera adjustment, camera vibration, and film processing. Resolu-tion is measured by examining a microfilmed resolution test chart under a microscope to determine the smallest pattern in which lines can be

distinguished both horizontally and vertically. (See resolution test pattern.)

resolution test pattern and chart
A carefully prepared chart containing a number of increasingly smaller test patterns. The pattern is a set of horizontal and vertical lines of specific size and spacing. The National Bureau of Standards "Microcopy Resolution Chart Number 1010a" is generally used in microfilming work.

retrieval, information
The recovering of desired information or data from a collection of documents or other records. The term information retrieval should be used as the generic term which includes reference, document, and fact retrieval.

retrieval coding
A term used to describe a system for retrieving specific images or data from microfilm. (See automatic coding, binary digital code, blip, code area, code line, document mark, flash index, film measure index, image mark retrieval code.)

retrieval system, information
A system for locating and selecting on demand, certain documents, data or other records relevant to given information from a file of material. Examples of information retrieval systems are classification, indexing, and machine searching systems. The term information retrieval system should be used as the generic term that includes reference, document, and fact retrieval systems.

reverse reading
A term used to define a reproduction which is a mirror image of the original,

e.g.,   ꟼ Я Ᵽ

(may be rotated to any position in the same plane).

right reading
That image which is legible in a normal reading position,

e.g.,   F R P

roll microfilm
A length of microfilm on a reel, spool or core.

roll-to-card printer
Equipment for producing duplicate card mounted microfilm from roll microfilm by contact printing.

roll-to-roll printer
An equipment for producing duplicate rolls of microfilm by contact printing.

195

rotary camera
See camera, rotary.

S

scanning device
(1) A mechanism found in certain microfilm readers where the entire image does not appear on the screen. The scanning device permits shifting the film or the entire optical system so that different portions of the microfilm frame or reel may be viewed.
*(2) A device that electrically dissects an image into sequential, contiguous lines, within each of which the sequential density variations are converted to analogous electrical variations.

screen, opaque
See opaque screen.

screen, translucent
See translucent screen.

sectioning (sectionalization)
Microfilming of an oversize document in two or more parts.

sensing mark
A mark on film or paper which activates an electrical device to perform an automatic function such as cutting of paper.

sensitize
(1) To treat a photographic layer with a chemical that makes it more photosensitive, or to extend the spectral sensitivity of a photosensitive layer by treating with dyes.
(2) To coat a support material with a photographic layer.
(3) To establish an electrostatic surface charge of uniform density on a photoconductor.

shelf life
The period of time before deterioration renders a material unusable.

silver film
See film, silver.

silver halide
A compound of silver and one of the following elements known as halogens: chlorine, bromine, iodine, fluorine.

silver recovery
The reclamation of silver from spent photographic fixing baths, an economic operation where large volumes of fixing baths are used. The silver may be precipitated by addition of sodium sulfide or zinc dust, or electrolytically deposited on cathodes suspended in the fixing bath. Silver recovery may destroy the photographic properties of the bath.

---

*Author's definition (unofficial)

simplex
An image positioning technique in rotary camera microfilming. Images are photographed across the full width of the film.

soft copy
An enlarged copy usually on a reader screen.

*software
The recorded information controlling the functioning of logic circuits or mechanisms in a computer or information processing device. It may be integral to the device (stored) or externally input, in either case the information has usually been recorded magnetically or as punched holes in paper cards or tape. The term is chosen to differentiate from "hardware"—i.e., the tangible, physical aspects of the information processing equipment.

sorter
An automatic machine used to arrange EAM cards in a predetermined sequence according to the punching in the cards.

*spatial cycle
The transition from one tonal state to another, and back to the original state within a given physical dimension of a graphic image—e.g. the complete cycle from black to white to black within a linear segment of a bar pattern.

speed
A common term for sensitivity of a photographic layer, maximum aperture of an objective lens, chemical efficiency of a processing solution or the timing of a shutter. The "speed" of film is established by American Standard procedures and is generally based on the reciprocal of the exposure required to produce a certain fractional gradient or density.

splice
A joint made by cementing or welding (heat splice) two pieces of film or paper together so they will function as a single piece when passing through a camera, processing machine, projector or other apparatus. Cemented splices are called lap splices since one piece overlaps the other. Most welds are called butt splices since the two pieces are butted together without any overlap. Some butt splices also use tape.

spool
A flanged holder on which unprocessed roll film is wound, designed to be inserted into cameras and processors. It is manufactured to close tolerances so that the film fits snugly within the flanges and keeps edge fog to a minimum. See American National Standards PH1.33, PH1.34, PH1.35 and PH1.36.

* SSTV (Slow Scan Television)
A television system in which the scanning process is slowed down to permit transmission of the picture signal over narrower band-width communication circuits; lacks the instantaneity of conventional TV, and is

---

*Author's definition (unofficial)

therefore confined to transmission of static (non-moving) images on a "time lapse" basis, as in facsimile communication.

strip film
Any short length of film too short to be wound on a reel, which is generally housed in a small can called a "strip" can or inserted in a jacket or other type of holder.

T

tabulating card
A card on which data is entered by use of punched holes or other means that can be sensed by a machine so that it can sort, collate, list, total or otherwise manipulate the card or the data.

target
(1) Any document or chart containing identification information, coding or test charts.
(2) An aid to technical or bibliographic control which is photographed on the film preceding or following the document. (Microfilm Norms, ALA.)

test chart
See resolution test pattern.

tonal range (tonal lattitude)
The relative ability of a light-sensitive material to reproduce accurately the varying tones between black and white. (See latitude.)

toner
The material employed to develop a latent xerographic image.

*TPC (Transparent Photo-Conductor)
A special, transparent microform base, which, in combination with a special electrostatic imaging system, permits the adding of new images to blank spaces on an existing microform (or the overprinting of existing images).

tracing
A translucent material suitable for reproduction on which the subject matter is rendered in pencil, ink, typing or printing.

trailer
That portion of film beyond the last images recorded.

translucent screen
A sheet of treated glass (ground, coated, etc.) or plastic used to form a visible image in microfilm readers. The image is projected onto the back of the screen and viewed from the front.

U

ultrafiche
Microfiche with images reduced more than 90X. (See microfiche, ultra high reduction, high reduction.)

198

ultraviolet
Pertaining to or designating those radiations which lie beyond the blue end of the visible spectrum, approximately from 2000 to 4000 nm. (2000 to 4000 angstroms.)

underdevelop
Insufficient development of sensitized material, due to developing for too short a time, use of a weakened developer, or too low a temperature.

underexpose
Insufficient exposure of sensitized material, due to insufficient illumination, too short an exposure time, or too small a lens aperture.

*unit carrier
Smallest physically divisible unit of a given microform—e.g., one reel, one fiche sheet, one EAM image card.

unitize
(1)   The separation of a roll of microfilm into individual frames and insertion in a carrier.
(2)   To microfilm on one or more sheets of microfiche a unit of information, such as a report, a specification or a periodical.

up
A term indicating one or more documents being in position to be photographed at the same time on the same frame, e.g., one up, two up, etc.

UV range (near)
The ultraviolet portion of the light spectrum immediately below the visual range extending from approximately 3200 to 4000 nm (3200 to 4000 angstroms).

V

very high reduction
Reductions above 60X up to and inclusive of 90X.

vesicular film
Film which has the light sensitive element suspended in a plastic layer and which upon exposure creates strains within the layer in the form of a latent image. The strains are released and the latent image made visual by heating the plastic layer. The image becomes permanent when the layer cools.

viewer
See hand viewer.

---

*Author's definition (unofficial)

199

visual range
The portion of light spectrum which can be seen by the human eye, which is approximately 4000 to 7000 nm (4000 to 7000 angstroms).

X

xerography (electrostatic)
A generic term for the formation of a latent electrostatic image by action of light on a photoconducting insulating surface. The latent image may be made visual by a number of methods such as applying charged pigmented powders or liquid which are attracted to the latent image. The particles either directly or by transfer may be applied and fixed to a suitable medium. See Webster's Unabridged Dictionary, Third Edition.

Appendix B
English/Metric Conversion Tables

I. WEIGHTS
1. English to Metric—
1 ounce (avoirdupois) = 28.35 grams
1 pound = 453.6 grams or 0.4536 kilograms
1 liquid pint = 0.473 liters
1 liquid quart = 0.946 liters

2. Metric to English—
1 gram = 0.035 oz. (avdp.)
1 kilogram = 2.205 lbs.
1 liter = 2.114 liquid pints or 1.06 liquid quarts

II. MEASURES
1. English to Metric—
(a) Length:

	Millimeters (mm)	Centimeters (cm)	Meter (m)
1/16 inch =	1.5875	0.1587	0.00158
1/8 inch =	3.175	0.3175	0.00317
1/4 inch =	6.35	0.635	0.00635
1/2 inch =	12.7	1.27	0.0127
1 inch =	25.4	2.54	0.0254
1 foot =	304.8	30.48	0.3048

(b) Area (desk- or floor-space):
1 square inch (in.^{2}) = 645 sq. mm; 6.45 sq. cm.; 0.000645 sq. m.
1 square foot (ft.^{2}) = 92903 sq. mm; 929 sq. cm.; 0.0929 sq. m.
(*Note:* to convert a given number of square inches or square feet to the metric equivalent area, simply use the above figures as multipliers.)

2. *Metric to English—*

(a)   Length:

	Inches	Foot (Feet)
1 millimeter (mm) =	0.039	0.00328
1 centimeter (cm) =	0.393	0.03281
1 meter (m)	= 39.37	3.281

(b)   Area (desk- or floor-space):
1 square millimeter (mm2) = 0.00155 sq. in.; 0.00001 sq. ft.
1 square centimeter (cm2) = 0.155 sq. in.; 0.00107 sq. ft.
1 square meter (m2) = 1550 sq. in.; 10.764 sq. ft.
(*Note:* to convert a given area in metric terms to square inches or square feet, simply use the above figures as multipliers.)

3. *English/Metric Equivalents for Some Common Micrographic Dimensions—*

(a)   Microform Dimensions:
16mm = 0.63 inch; 35mm = 1.38 inches; 105mm = 4.14 inches; 148mm = 5.83 inches; 100 ft. = 30.48 meters.

(b)   Film Thicknesses:
1 mil (1/1000-inch) = 0.0254mm; 2.5 mils = 0.0635mm; 3 mils = 0.0762mm; 5 mils = 0.127mm; 7 mils = 0.178mm

(c)   Document Dimensions:
8-1/2 in. = 216mm or 21.6cm; 11 in. = 279.4mm or 27.9cm; 14 in. = 355.6mm or 35.6cm; 17 in. = 432mm or 43.2cm.

(d)   Data Densities:
800 bits per inch (bpi) = 31.5 bits per mm or 315 bits per cm.
1600 bpi = 63 bits per mm or 630 bits per cm.

Appendix C
Published Standards By Category

What follows is as comprehensive a list as possible of published micrographic standards that are available to the public as of late 1975. The list is divided into appropriate categories, and the sources of the listed standards are coded as follows:

AFN—
Association Francaise de Normalisation
Service des Ventes, Tour Europe
92-Courbevoie, Paris, France

ANSI—
American National Standards Institute, Inc.
1430 Broadway, New York, N. Y. 10018

ECMA—
European Computer Manufacturers Association
114 Rue du Rhone, 1204 Geneva, Switzerland

EIA—
Electronic Industries Association
2001 Eye St., N.W., Washington, D.C. 20006

E-K—
Eastman Kodak Co.
(contact nearest branch office)

GPO—
Superintendent of Documents
U.S. Government Printing Office
Washington, D.C. 20402

IEEE—
Institute of Electrical & Electronic Engineers, Inc.
(Standards Office) 345 E. 47th St.
New York, N.Y. 10017

ISO—
International Organization for Standardization
(standards available from ANSI. See above.)

MIL,
FED-
(U.S. Government standards)
Commanding Officer (Code 105), Naval Publications
& Forms Center, 5801 Tabor Ave.
Philadelphia, Pa. 19120

MUN—
Munsell Color Co., Inc.
2441 N. Calvert St.
Baltimore, Md. 21218

NBS—
National Bureau of Standards (U.S.)
Office of Standard Reference Materials
Washington, D.C. 20224

NMA— National Micrographics Association
8728 Colesville Road
Silver Spring, Md. 20910
UN— Documentation Div., Hammarskjold Library
United Nations, New York, N.Y. 10017

Following the source code in each case is the identifying number (or other designation) under which the standard is published and by which it is normally indexed and referenced.

1. CHARACTERS, SYMBOLS, DRAFTING

NMA MS4-1972, ANSI PH 5.17-1973,	Flowchart Symbols and Their Usage in Micrographics
NMA MS101-1969	Microfont (set of 4 charts)
NMA MS102-1972,	Drafting Guide for Microfilm
NMA MS107-1973,	Flowchart Symbols Template
NMA RS3-1971,	"Modern Drafting Techniques for Quality Microreproductions" by Carl E. Nelson
ANSI X3.5-1970,	Flowchart Symbols and Their Usage in Information Processing, Specifications For
ANSI X3.17-1966,	Character Set for Optical Character Recognition
ISO R435-1965,	ISO Conventional Typographical Character For Legibility Tests
ISO R1073-1969,	Alphanumeric Character Sets for Optical Recognition
ECMA-11 (Oct. 1971),	European Computer Manufacturers Association Standard for the Alphanumeric Character Set OCR-B for Optical Recognition

2. COM

NMA MS1-1971,	Quality Standards for Computer Output Microfilm
NMA MS2-1971,	Format and Coding for Computer Output Microfilm

3. EQUIPMENT

ANSI PH5.1-1970,	Microfilm Readers for 16 mm and 35 mm Film on Reels, Specifications for
ANSI PH5.7-1970,	Micro-Opaque Readers, Specifications for
MIL-V-80240 (10/27/72), Amendment 1 (2/5/73),	Viewer, Microfiche (48X)
MIL-V-80241 (9/15/72), Amendment 1 (2/14/73),	Viewer/Printer, Microfiche (48X)
ISO R452-1965,	Essential Characteristics of 35 mm Microfilm Reading Apparatus

4. FILM, MICROFORMS
(a)   Aperture & Copy Cards

NMA MS9-1973,
ANSI PH5.12-1973,   Method for Measuring Thickness of Buildup Area on Unitized Microfilm Carriers (Aperture, Camera, Copy and Image Cards)*

NMA MS10-1973,
ANSI PH5.14-1973,   Method for Determining Adhesion of Protection Sheet to Aperture Adhesive of Unitized Microfilm Carrier (Aperture Card)

ANSI PH5.8-1971,   Unitized Microfilm Carriers (Aperture, Camera, Copy and Image Cards), Dimensions for

ANSI X3.11-1969,   General Purpose Paper Cards for Information Processing, Specifications for

ANSI X3.21-1967,   Rectangular Holes in Twelve-Row Punched Cards

MIL-C-9877B (5/8/64),
Amendment 1 (8/15/66),   Cards, Aperture
MIL-C-9949 (11/1/62),
Amendment 3 (10/3/66),   Cards, Copy
MIL-STD-804B (8/15/66),   Format and Coding of Tabulating and Aperture Cards for Engineering Data Micro-Reproduction System

FED G-C-116d (4/66),   Cards, Tabulating

(b)   Copy film
FED L-F-315C (11/15/71),   Film, Direct Positive, Roll (Diazo Type)
FED L-F-320C (11/17/72),   Film, Thermal Developing
FED L-F-340B (3/29/73),   Film, Diazo Type, Sensitized, Moist and Dry Process, Roll and Sheet

(c)   Microfiche
NMA MS5-1972,   Microfiche of Documents
NMA RS14-1975,   User's Guide to Standard Microfiche Formats
ANSI PH5.9-1970,   Microfiche, Specifications for
MIL-M-38748A (12/1/70),   Microfiche for Engineering/Technical Data, Reports, Studies and Related Data, Requirements for

MIL-M-63048 (TM),
(3/15/71),   Preparation of Equipment Publications on Microfiche
MIL-F-80242 (3/15/74),   Film, Microfiche, 48X
ISO 2707-1973,   Transparent A6 Size Microfiche of Uniform Division—Image Arrangements No.

---

*A *camera card* is an aperture card containing unexposed silver-halide film, and an *image card* is a camera, aperture or copy card containing a processed microimage.

205

	1 and No. 2
ISO 2708-1973,	Transparent A6 Size Microfiche of Variable Division—Image Arrangements A and B
UN ST/PB/28 (1968),	United Nations Microfiche Standard

(d) Roll Film

ANSI PH1.13-1971,	Cores for Photographic Film Rolls (Plastic, Wood, or Metal), Dimensions for
ANSI PH1.33-1972,	16 mm 100-Foot, 16 mm 200-Foot, 35 mm 100-Foot, and 70 mm 100-Foot Spools for Recording Instruments and for Microfilm and Still-Picture Cameras, Dimensions for
ANSI PH5.3-1973,	16 mm and 35 mm Silver-Gelatin Microfilms for Reel Applications, Specifications for
ANSI PH5.6-1974,	100-Foot Reels for Processed 16 mm and 35 mm Microfilm, Dimensions for
MIL-M-46849 (12/15/71),	Microfilming of Engineering and Related Documents, 16 mm, Requirements for
FED L-F-334d (5/15/67),	Film, Photographic, Roll, Microfilm (Black and White)
ISO R1116-1969,	35 mm and 16 mm Microfilm, Spools and Reels

(e) Miscellaneous

NMA MS110-1974,	Recommended Practice for Operational Procedures for the Production of Microforms
ANSI PH1.19-1969,	Emulsion Side of Photographic Sheet Films, Designation of
ANSI PH1.25-1974,	Safety Photographic Film, Specifications for
FED NO. 125B (3/21/72),	Film Photographic and Film Photographic Processed, (For Permanent Record Use)
FED No. 170B (3/8/71),	Film Photographic, Black and White, Classification and Testing Methods
ISO R169-1960,	Sizes of Photocopies (on paper) Readable Without Optical Devices
ISO 2803-1974,	Archival Microfilm

5. INSPECTION, TESTING, MEASURING

NMA MS104-1972,	Recommdended Practice for Inspection and Quality Control of First Generation Silver Halide Microfilm
NMA MS105-1972,	Microfiche Grid Gauge, 98 Frame, 24X
NMA MS108-1973,	Microfiche Grid Gauge, 270 Frame, 48X
NMA MS 109-1973,	Microfiche Test Target
NBS SRM 1010a,	Microcopy Resolution Test Charts (sets of five charts)

NBS SRM 1008,	Calibrated Photographic Step Tablet 0-4, Type Visual VI b
NBS SRM 1009,	Calibrated Photographic Step Tablet 0-3, Type Visual VI-6
ANSI PH1.28-1973,	Photographic Film for Archival Records, Silver-Gelatin Type, or Cellulose Ester Base, Specifications for
ANSI PH1.29-1971,	Curl of Photographic Film, Methods for Determining
ANSI PH1.31-1973,	Brittleness of Photographic Film, Method for Determining
ANSI PH1.32-1973,	Determining the Dimensional Change Characteristics of Photographic Films and Papers, Methods for
ANSI PH1.37-1969,	Scratch Resistance of Processed Photographic Film, Methods for Determining
ANSI PH1.41-1973,	Photographic Film for Archival Records, Silver-Gelatin Type, on Polyester Base, Specifications for
ANSI PH2.19-1959,	Diffuse Transmission Density
ANSI PH2.25-1965,	Photographic Printing Density (Carbon Step Tablet Method)
ANSI PH4.8-1971,	Methylene Blue Method for Measuring Thiosulfate, and Silver Densitometric Method for Measuring Residual Chemicals in Films, Plates and Papers
MIL-STD-21319 (4/15/60),	Gauge, Aperture Card, No. 201-1
MIL-STD-27210 (7/16/62),	Density Step Wedge
ISO R5-1955,	Diffuse Transmission Density (See ANSI PH2.19)
ISO R417-1965,	Methods for Determining Thiosulphate and Tetrathronate in Processed Black and White Photographic Film, Plates and Papers (see ANSI PH4.8)
ISO R446-1965,	Microcopies, Legibility Tests: Description and Use of the ISO Mire (ISO Test Object) for Checking a Reading Apparatus
ISO R689-1968,	Microcopies, Legibility Tests: Description and Use of the ISO Micromire (Micro Test Object) for Checking a Reading Apparatus
AFN NFZ43-007,	Mire Test Object
MUN 8-7,	Neutral Density Test Cards, 6" x 6" (Components of Test Targets per MIL-M-9868: 6, 25 and 50 percent reflectance)
E-K 1990019, 1990050, 1990076,	Recordak Reference Targets, 16, 24 and 30X respectively, per MIL-M-9868
E-K 1990035, 1990092,	Recordak Reference Targets, 20 and 36X respectively
E-K	Special Calibrated Photographic Step Tablet # 3

E-K 1598515,	Recordak Fine Grain Control Strips 7457 (16 mm x 100-foot roll)
E-K 1555952,	Recordak AHU Control Strips 7460 (16mm x 100-foot roll)
E-K 1596097,	Recordak Dacomatic A Control Strips 7461 (16 mm x 100-foot roll)
E-K 1541200,	Recordak AHU Control Strips 5460 (35 mm x 100-foot roll)

6. MICROFILMING, GENERAL

MIL-M-9868D (10/1/70),	Microfilming of Engineering Documents, 35 mm, Requirements for
MIL-P-9879A (12/1/62), Amendment 1 (12/6/66),	Photographing of Construction/Architectural Drawings, Maps and Related Documents, 105 mm, Requirements for
MIL-M-38761 (8/15/66), Amendment 1 (10/1/70),	Microfilming and Photographing of Engineering/Technical Data and related Documents; PCAM Card Preparation, Engineering Data Micro-Reproduction System, General Requirements for Preparation of
MIL-HDBK-303 (9/15/64),	Micro-Reproduction of Engineering Documents
GPO 3000-0055,	Specifications for the Microfilming of Newspapers in the Library of Congress
GPO 3000-00068,	Specifications for the Microfilming of Books and Pamphlets in the Library of Congress

7. REMOTE ACCESSING

NMA MS3-1972, ANSI C16.45-1973,	Facsimile Transmission of Microfilmed Documents
EIA RS-328,	Message Facsimile Equipment for Operation on Switched Voice Facilities Using Data Communication Terminal Equipment
EIA RS-357,	Interface Between Facsimile Terminal Equipment and Voice Frequency Data Communication Terminal Equipment
EIA RS-373,	Unattended Operation of Facsimile Equipment
EIA RS-247,	Analog-to-Digital Conversion Equipment
EIA RS-312-A,	Engineering Specification Format for Monochrome, CCTV Camera Equipment
EIA RS-343-A,	Electrical Performance Standards for High Resolution CCTV Camera
EIA RS-412-A,	Electrical Performance Standards for Direct View High Resolution Monochrome CCTV Monitors

EIA Bulletin #1,	Closed Circuit Television Definitions
IEEE STD 167-1966,	
ANSI C16.37-1971,	Facsimile, Test Procedures for
IEEE 167-A,	Facsimile Test Chart (High Definition)
IEEE STD 168,	Facimile, Definition of Terms for

8. *VOCABULARY, DEFINITIONS*

NMA MS100-1971,	Glossary of Micrographics (5th Ed.)
ANSI X3.12-1970,	Vocabulary for Information Processing
MIL-HDBK-25A	
(1/19/71),	Glossary of Photographic Terms

9. *MISCELLANEOUS*

NMA MS6-1974,	Microfilm Package Labeling
NMA MS8-1974,	
ANSI PH5.20-1974	Document Mark (Blip) Used in Image Mark Retrieval Systems
ANSI PH4.20-1970,	Photographic Filing Enclosures for Storing Processed Photographic Films, Plates, and Papers, Requirements for
ANSI PH5.2-1970,	Paper Sheets for Photo-Reproductions of Documents, Dimensions of
MIL-STD-100A (10/1/69),	Engineering Drawing Practices

INDEX

212

Department of Defense (DOD), 55, 69, 94, 120
Department store, use of micrographics in, 27
Depreciation, depreciation accounting, 94(fn), 95, 165
  cash flow, 95
  government guidelines, 95
  straight line, 95
Design considerations, micrographic file, 136-141
Design, system, 86, 119-156,
  general considerations, 148-156
Desk-top reader, 18, 114, 141, 142
Desk, use of microforms at, 18, 38, 114, 140, 141, 142, 145
Destruction of documents, 1, 35, 105, 133
Detection, error, COM, 130
Detection, theft, 139
Developer, copy film, 135
  print, 18, 145
Development,
  film, 82, 111-112, 135
  print, 84
Diazo film, 15, 59, 81, 82, *83,* 111-112, 131-132, 134-135, 152
Diazo printing process, 78
Digital data, 60(pc), 61, 97, 102, 108, 136
  compression, 108
  in CIM, 57, 59, 60(pc)
  in COM, 10, 98, 101, 102
Digital format, 61-62
Digital storage, 59
Dimensional stability, 76
Direct duplicating film, 82
Directory, telephone, in microform, 48, 81, 142
"Direct sign", 82
Disaster file, 35-36, 61, 93
Disaster, insurance against, 25-26, 30, 36, 138, 139, 165
Disc, magnetic, 57, 59, 128(fn)
Discoloration of prints, 84, 85
Display device, electronic, 10, 164
Display and reproduction equipment, 2, 18, 19-22, 113-116, 125, 141
Disposal, processing wastes, 15, 101, 130
Dissipation, heat, 149
Distribution, 82, 140
  as element of basic system, 2
  considerations, 122-123
  cost of, 94, 113, 122, 123, 140
  high volume, 123, 131, 132
  machine-aided, 59
  selective, 59
  semi-automated, 132
  speed of, 29
Documentation

engineering, quality requirements for, 80
  scientific, 80
  support, 137
Document illumination, 10
Document index, 33
Document mobility, 76
Documents, letter-size, 5, 101, 108, 109, 122(fn), 123
Document size, 5, 76, 84, 101, 107, 108, 109
Documents, preparation of, for microfilming, 104, *151,* 159
Documents, re-issuing of, 33, 120
Drafting, 128-129
Drawings,
  architectural, 76
  "bedsheet" size, 76
  line, 81
Dry print processes, 84, 85, 116, 145
  dry silver, 85, 116
  electrostatic, 84, 116
Dual-image reader, 116
Duo microimage format, *5*
Duplex microimage format, *5*
Duplication of microimages, 2, 7, 15, 38, 82, *83,* 132, 140,
  by outside vendor, 101, 102, 103-104, 110, 111, 112, 113
  contract, 15, 37, 59, 80, 81(fn), 102, 110, 112
  defined, 37
  demand, 15, 25-26, 110, 122, 136, 141
  in aperture cards, 15, 59, 141
  in color, 87
  in-house versus outside, 131, 132
  multi-image, 7, 90, 122
  production(bulk), 15, 122, 131-132, 135
  quality control, 134-135, 141, *151*
  wasteful, 122
Duplicator, microform, *16-17,* 93, 131, 135, 141
  demand, 136
  programmable, 132
  selection of, 131-132
Durability, equipment, 95
Dust, effect of on microimages, 80, 81, 125
Dynamic file, 36

E

Economic analysis, 95-97, 165
Economic elements, micrographic system, 93
Economic feasibility, 95
Economics
  general, 93-97
  paper versus micrographics, 93, 94, 104-105, 123, 164
Editing, electronic, 57, *60*

216

217

dry silver paper, 85
vesicular film, 15, 82, 111, 135
Heat dissipation, 149
Height, equipment, restriction of, 138
Hollerith keypunch sensing, 59
Hospital, use of micrographics in, 28
Human-computer interaction, 128, 148
Human handling of microforms, 45, 88,
  108
Hypo (fixer), 133

I

Illumination
  of documents for filming, 10
  of microimages, for viewing, printing,
    9, 18, 116, 124, 135, 142, 143(pc), 145
Image area, 112
Image arrangements, *5,* 101, 102, 106
Image background, 81, 131
Image cards, 8, 30, 59, 106, 107, 111, 113,
  121, 123, 137
Image contrast, 5, 84, 133, 135, 141, 146
Image formats, 5, 120, 124
Image, latent, *83,* 84-85
"Image", magnetic, 57
Image monitoring, COM, 130
Image orientation, 5, 7
Image permanence, 127, 133
Image placement on film, 5, 7
Image plane, 44
Image scanner, 61, 62, *64,* 88
Image sequence, 5, 120
Image sharpness, 145, 146
Image size, 125
Image superimposition, 120, 135
Image tonality, 82, 131
Imaging, add-on, 87
Impact printing, 55, 94, 101
Imperfections, microform, 131, 134
Implementation scheduling, 157-159
Implementation, system, 94, 117, 163
Impulses, electrical, 51, 57, 61
"Inactive" information, 2
Index
  automated, 53
  document, 33
  image address, 42
  keyword, 33
  look-up, 146
Indexing
  marks, 42(pc)
  of documents, 33
  of microforms, eye-readable, 36
  of microforms, on film, 42
  visual, 42-43
Indicator, on-film, 41-43
Individual character legibility, 84, 88,
  109, 125
Industrial organizations, standards activities of, 67-68

Industry, micrographics, 67
Information retrieval, 33, 52
Information system, 1
Information transfer, 60-65
Infringement, copyright, 90-91
Input, system, nature of, 76-77, 81
Inspection apparatus, microform, 93,
  116, 133, 136
Inspection facilities, 133
Inspection,
  visual (of microforms), 135, 141
Integral microform storage, 45, 50, 52
Integral positional locating (in auto-
  mated fiche readers), 120-121
Interaction, human-computer, 128, 129
Interactive computer terminals, 52, *53,*
  128-129
Interface, computer, 31
Interfiling, mixed microforms, 50
Interlibrary loans, 90-91
Intermediate master, 82
International Standards Organization
  (ISO), 7, 69-70, 71(pc)
Interpreting of EAM cards, 59
  equipment for, 116, 124, 136
Isolation of files, 39, 105

J

Jacket-filling apparatus, 116, 136
Jackets, 7-8, 9, 28, 116, 122
  updating of, 87
  use of, in systems, 28, 94, 116

K

Keyboard, manual selector, 30, 31, 45, 51,
  52, 61
Keying, manual, for automated retrieval,
  30-31, 36, 44, 45, 50, 52, 64(pc), 65, 120,
  139
Keypunching of EAM cards, 49, 59, 146
  equipment for, 116, 124, 136, 148
Keypunch reproduction, 59, 124, 136
Keypunch sensing, Hollerith, 59
Keyword index, 33
Keywords, use of, 33, 52

L

Labels, film carton, 101-102, 137
Labor requirements, 93, 99, 131, 137, 146
  apportionment of, 146
  clerical, 97
  level of skill, 146
Labor, saving of, 26, 30, 94, 96
Ladder, use of microform reader on, *76-*
  77
Language, code, 52
"Lap" reader, 114

"Morgue", newspaper, in microform, 52
Motorized advance, 43, 44
Mounter, film, 116, 124, 136
Mounting, film to aperture cards, 59, 135
Multi-image duplication, 7, 90, 122
Multi-media reader, 18, 114, 145
Multiple film plane technique, 120-121

N

National Bureau of Standards (NBS), U.S., 69
  microcopy resolution test chart, 69, *70*, 73, 78-80, 135
NBS resolution test pattern, 69, *70*, 71(pc), 73, 78-80, 135
"Need-to-know" security, 139
"Negative-appearing" images, 82, *83*, 84, 102, 131
Newspaper microfilming, 9
Newspaper pages in microform, 5, 9, 70, 81, 82, 134, 140-141, 142
Newspaper "morgue" in microform, 52
NMA (National Micrographics Association), 3, 7, 67, 68-69, 70, 84, 85(pc), 126, 134, 152, 154, 159
  Computer Image Processing (CIP) division, 68
  standards activities of, 68-69
Nonfilm microimages, 1, 9
Nonoptical retrieval, 44,
Nonperforated film, 5
Nonreversal versus nonreversing, explanation, 81(fn)
Nonstandard microforms, 9, 50, 122, 125
"Nuisances" encountered in filming, 104
Number List, resolving of, 80

O

Objectives, system, 164-166
Obsolescence, equipment, 95, 99
OCR (Optical Character Recognition), 61
Odometer, 41-42
Office copier, 61, 88
Office furniture, 95, 149-152, 158(pc)
1:1 reproduction, 37, 78, 82, 142
On-film indicator, 41-43
On-Line versus off-line, 57, 129
Operating space, equipment, 96, 130, 148-149
Operational considerations, micrographic systems, 159
Operational procedures, 159
Operations responsibility, 159
Operator,
  camera, 148
  CIM device, 57
  COM device, 148
  keypunch, 148

microreproduction equipment, 148
processor, 146, 148
Optical Character Recognition (OCR), 61
Optical filter, 133
Optical retrieval, 44-45, 48
Optics, optical system,
  of a microform reader, 18
  of a scanning system, 62, 88
  precision of, 76
  resolving capability of, 180
Ordinances,
  safety, ammonia usage, 132
  waste disposal, 15, 101, 130
Organizational "umbrella", 136, 159
Organization, file, 137, 138
Organizations, standards,
  government, 67, 69, 73
  industrial, 67, 68
  professional, 67-70, 73
Orientation, image, 5, 7
Originals (original documents),
  filing of, 104-105, 128
  grouping of, for microfilming, 37-38, 104
  nature of, 26(fn), 76-77, 81(fn), 84, 107, 108, 109
  revision of, 87, 120, 128-129, 140
OSHA safety requirements, 152
Out-of-file delays, 25
Output, system, nature of, 77-78, 87, 126, 136, 140-141, 148
Overlay, forms (COM), 56, 102, 129

P

Packing density,
  magnetic tape, 102, 129
  microimages, 123
Page capacities, microform, 106
Page "marking", 33
Paper, electroconductive, 84
Paper, generation of, 93
Paper originals, 26(fn), 97, 104-105
Paper, photosensitive, 85
Paper, print, 18, 78, 116, 145
  characteristics of, 84-85
  types of (processes), 84-85
Paper, silver-halide, 84
Paper-to-paper reproduction, 78, 111.
Paper versus micrographics, *105*, 113, 140, 164
  economics of, 93, 94, 104-105, 123, 164
  in data processing, 128
  in word processing, 129
"Pantograph", 43
Parcel rate, 123
Parts catalogs in microform, 29
"Passwords", 61
Patch, test, reflectance, 134-135
Pattern, resolution test, 79-80

production, criteria for, 73-74, 133-13[141
resolution, 69
Quality, microimage
archival, 127-128, 131, 133
legal requirements, 80, 89
loss of, 77, 78
Quality rating, ammonia gas, 111-112
Quality, reproduction, 78-80, 125
Quality requirements, 80, 89, 103, 104, 131
Quality standards, 133-134
Quality, system,
input, 76-77
output, 77-85, 124-125
Quantities,
equipment, 111, 141
materials, 111-113
Quantities versus weight, microforms, 113, 123
Questionnaire, use of, 85
Queuing, 86, 105, 128
delays due to, 105, 138
Quotation, request for, 101

R

Random, filing, 31, 87, 138
Range, tonal, 5
Rate, bulk (mail), 29, 113, 123
Rate, parcel, 123
Rates, communication, 110
Ratio, enlargement, 82
Ratio, reduction, 80, 88, 136-137
"Raw" film, 4
RCA Corporation, 84(fn)
Recognition, character, optical (OCR), 61
Readability,
effect of magnification on, 142
impairment of, 80, 125, 133
standards for, 125
Reader, automated, 45
Reader-printers, microform, 18, *21,* 26, 93, 94, 113-116, 124, 135, 136, 140, 141-146
Readers, microform, 2, 18, *19-20,* 26, 27, 28, 30, 37, 41, 43, 45, 70, 93, 94, 113-116, 124, 135, 136, 140, 141-145, 164, 165
battery-operated, 77
central reference ("large screen"), 114, 116
collapsible, 114
comfort in use of, 80, 142, 145
cost of, 95, 113-114
desk-top, 18, 114, 141, 142
dual-image, 116
ladder, 76-77
"lap" (portable), 114
motorized, 27, 36, 41, 43, 114

multimedia, 18, 114, 145
prolonged use of, 80, 141, 142
requirements of, 141-145
scanning type, 76, 142
screenless, 142, *144*
screen size, 18, 141-142
selection of, 141-145
shared use, 141-142, 145, 146
size of, 141-142
types of (input), 145
"Real time", 64(pc)
Recording, magnetic, 57
Records,
generation of, 137
microfilming of, 27, 28, 81, 94
warehousing of, 36, 105
Recovery, silver, 131
Reductions, filming, 10, 18, 84, 88, 101, 102, 104, 120-121, 122(fn), 123, 124, 125, 136, 137
linear, 79-80
test for, 134
Redundancy (in filing), 137, 138, 139, 153(pc)
partial, 139
Reel, 4, 48, 73
Reference file, 37, 136, 140-141
Reference versus reproduction, 37, 80-81, 136, 140
Refiling effort, 94, 97
Reflectance test patches, 134-135
Reflection, light, 9(pc)
Re-issuing of documents, 33, 120
single-sheet, 120
Re-issuing of microforms, 87
Remote-controlled zoom, CCTV, 64
Remotecopier, 61
Replenishment, processing chemicals, 127, 131
Reports in microform, 140
Representative systems, flowcharts of, *27-29, 31, 32*
Reproduction of microimages, 76-85
defined, 37
legal aspects, 89-91
reference versus, 37, 80-81, 136, 140
Reproduction of keypunching, 59, 124, 136
Reproduction, 1:1, 37, 78, 82, 142
Reproduction, paper-to-paper, 78, 111
Reproduction quality, 78-80, 125
Request for Quotation (RFQ), 101
Requirements, legal, 89
Requirements, system, 2, 116, 140
equipment, 2, 105, 111, 113, 116, 124, 137, 138, 141, 152
material, 124
quality, 103, 104, 131
Research, micrographics as an aid to, 26, 129

The following companies have provided photographs of their equipment for use in this book: Bell and Howell Company, Dukane Corporation, Eastman Kodak Co., Image Systems Inc., Microtech Press, Inc., NCR Corporation, Taylor Merchant Corp., Washington Scientific Industries, Inc., Criterion Micrographics, Inc., Microvision, Inc., Itek Graphic Products, 3M Microfilm Systems, A-M Bruning Division, Dietzgen Corporation, Terminal Data Corporation, Oscar Fisher Company, Inc., Technology Incorporated, Kalvar Corporation, Microba Corporation, Scott Graphics, Inc., and their cooperation is gratefully acknowledged.